MW00595896

Zoology 2 Notebooking Journal

for

Exploring Creation with Zoology 2: Swimming Creatures

by
Jeannie Fulbright

Zoology 2 Notebooking Journal

Published by
Apologia Educational Ministries, Inc.
1106 Meridian Plaza, Suite 220/340
Anderson, IN 46016

www.apologia.com

Manufactured in the United States of America
9th Printing, February 2018

ISBN: 978-1-935495-12-3

Printed by LSC Communications

Cover Design by Kim Williams

All Biblical quotations are from the New American Standard Bible, King James Version, New International Version or New King James Version

Photo Credits

All images used with permission/license from Jupiter images except the images listed below:

Rebecca Purifoy: pp. 14, 72, 179, A 8

Megan Whitaker: pp. 84, 111

FCIT: pp. 164, 165

Crestock.com: A1, A5, A11, A13, A21, A25, A27, A31, A33, A35, A47, A49, A51
Niles Biological: A43
Thinkstock.com: A12 (istockphoto), A17 (istockphoto), A19 (Hemera), A41 (right: istockphoto) (left: Comstock), A51 (Jupiterimages), A53 (Top: Hemera, Middle: Comstock, Bottom: istockphoto), A55 (Comstock) A56 (Left and Middle: Comstock, Middle Right and Right: istockphoto) A58 (Left and Left Middle: Comstock, Right Middle: istockphoto, Right: Comstock) A59 (Photodisc, Ablestock, Jupiter Images, Medioimages/Photodisc, A59 (Comstock), A59 (Adam Laverty)

Fonts used with permission/license from:

HWT Manuscript , Abeka Cursive – **Educational Fontware**
Sepulcra - **Abel P. Delgado**
Myfonts.com: Acorn Initials – **Typographer Mediengestaltung**; Airmole, Almonte – **Ray Larabie**; Intellectual Borders, Bailarina – **Intellectua Designs**; Bubble Man – **Brain Eaters**; Daylilies **Will-Harris (Sutcliffe)**; Dragoon- **Gyrl Friday**; Kingthings Willow - **Cheapprofonts**; LTC Fournier – **P22 Type Foundry**; Leafy Stencil – **Character**; MFC Franklin Corners – **Monogram Fonts**; MarieBalleIntitials – **Art types**;Message of the Bids – **Chicken**; Novella – **Font Haus**; Plantegenet Cherokee; River City Sandwriting – **Rivercity Fonts**; Treasury Gold – **Canada Type**; Turtle Black Shadow – **Otto Maur**; Mirage Bazaar, Vegas Caravan – **Fontdiner.com**; Waltari - **Heinz König**; Zapfino – **Linotype Library**; Puzzle Pieces -**Samuel MARCIUS**

Note from the Author

Welcome to the wonderful adventure in learning called "Notebooking." This notebooking journal correlates with Apologia's *Exploring Creation with Zoology 2,* by Jeannie Fulbright. The activities in this journal provide everything your child needs to complete the assignments in *Exploring Creation with Zoology 2* and more. It will serve as your child's individual notebook. You only need to provide scissors, glue, colored pencils, a stapler and a few brass fasteners.

The concept of notebooking is not a new one. In fact, keeping notebooks was the primary way the learned men of our past educated themselves, from Leonardo Da Vinci and Christopher Columbus to George Washington, John Quincy Adams and Meriwether Lewis. These men and many others of their time were avid notebookers. As we know, they were also much more advanced in their knowledge—even as teens—than we are today. George Washington was a licensed surveyor during his teenage years, and John Quincy Adams graduated from law school at age 17.

It would be wise for us to emulate the methods of education of these great men, rather than the failing methods used in our schools today. Common modern methods, namely fill-in-the-blank and matching worksheets, do not fully engage the student's mind. Studies show that we remember only 5% of what we hear, 50% of what we see and hear and 90% of what we see, hear and do. When we participate in activities that correspond with learning, we increase our retention exponentially. This is exactly what the Zoology 2 Notebooking Journal is designed to do—offer engaging learning activities to increase your student's retention.

The National Center for Educational Statistics shows us that American school children, by twelfth grade, rank at the bottom of international assessments, and do not even know 50% of what students in top-ranked countries know. As home educators, we have the opportunity to discard methods that are detrimental and ineffective and adopt the methods that will genuinely educate our children.

In addition to academic achievement, notebooking offers many benefits to students and parents. For students, it provides an opportunity to uniquely express themselves as they learn. It also provides a treasured memento of educational endeavors. For parents, it is a record of the year's studies and can easily be transferred to a portfolio if needed.

This journal will make notebooking easier for both you and your student by supplying a plethora of templates, hands-on crafts and projects, additional experiment ideas, and many activities that will engage your student in learning. It will prove invaluable in helping students create a wonderful keepsake of all they learned in zoology 2. Remember that *everything in this notebooking journal is optional*. Because it will serve as your student's own unique notebook, you may customize it by simply tearing out the activity pages that you choose not to use. You, as the teacher, will decide what truly benefits your student's learning experience, encourages a love for learning and builds his confidence in science. Every child is different, learns differently and will respond differently to the array of activities provided here. Use discernment in how many of the activities and assignments you use with your child. Your goal is not to complete every activity but to make learning a joy.

However, as a seasoned home educator, let me encourage you not to attempt to do every single activity in this notebooking journal. Choose the projects and activities that will be enjoyable and inspire a love of learning. If something is a drudgery, it will not serve to increase your student's retention, but will only discourage his enjoyment of science–resulting in an unmotivated learner.

It is my hope and prayer that you and your students will benefit from your studies this year, growing closer to God as you learn of His creation, and finding joy in the learning process.

Warmly,

Table of Contents

Table of Contents

Zoology 2 Notebooking Journal

Below are descriptions of a suggested schedule and the activities included in this notebooking journal. The first three activities are taken directly from the coursework contained in *Exploring Creation with Zoology 2.* The others are additional optional activities coordinating with the book.

Suggested Schedule

A suggested schedule for reading the *Exploring Creation with Zoology 2* text and completing the activities contained in the book and in this journal has been provided. Though not every student or parent will choose to utilize the schedule, those who do may find it very beneficial. Some parents will appreciate having their student's daily reading and assignments organized for them. Older students will find it easy to complete the book and journal by following the schedule on their own. Though the suggested schedule provides for the zoology 2 course to be completed in twenty-eight weeks, two days per week, it is flexible and can be made to fit your goals. The course can be expedited by completing three or four days of science per week. You can lengthen the course by studying science only one day per week. If you wish to do the extra activities found in the Dive Deeper pages, still another day of science can be added. Above all, use the suggested schedule in a way that best suits your family.

Fascinating Facts

Exploring Creation with Zoology 2 contains many facts, ideas and interesting notions. Although oral (verbal) narration is an effective means for retention, your student may wish to record some of the information either through drawing or writing. The Fascinating Facts pages can be used for written narrations. Some of the lessons provide two Fascinating Facts pages for your student's use. If your student is an avid writer, you can access more Fascinating Facts pages to print (free of charge) on the Apologia website. To do so, simply login to www.apologia.com/bookextras and type in this password: Godmadethemswim. These additional pages can be included in this notebooking journal by simply stapling them onto one of the existing Fascinating Facts pages.

What Do You Remember? Review Questions

These review questions are the same questions asked in the "What Do You Remember?" section found in each lesson of the book. They can be answered orally (verbally) or, for older students, as a written narration assignment. For co-ops or classroom use, these questions may also serve as a way to evaluate how much the students have retained from the reading. However, I would encourage you to review the material with the students before giving the questions as a written narration assignment. This will encourage better retention of the material and increase both the students' confidence and their ability to restate their learning. The answers to the review questions can be found on pages 219 through 223 of *Exploring Creation with Zoology 2.*

Notebooking Assignments, Activities and Projects

The lessons in *Exploring Creation with Zoology 2* offer suggested notebooking assignments, activities and projects typically found at the end of each lesson. Provided in this journal are templates (blank pages with lines for writing or space for drawing) which your student can use for completing these activities. Colored pencils can be used to encourage creative, high quality work. Some projects require the student to use a Scientific Speculation Sheet. These sheets have been included in this notebooking journal. Drawings or pictures of the projects can be pasted onto the Scientific Speculation Sheets.

Scripture Copywork

Incorporating the Word of God in your science studies through Scripture Copywork will provide many benefits to your student. It will encourage stronger faith and memorization of Scripture, as well as better writing, spelling and grammar skills. Each lesson has a corresponding verse for your child to copy, which may be printed or written in cursive.

Vocabulary Crosswords

If you desire to expand your child's studies with vocabulary activities, the Vocabulary Crosswords can be used to review the new words and concepts mentioned in the lesson. Remember, working with the vocabulary in this manner is not a "test" of your child's knowledge, but should be viewed as a reinforcement and reminder of what he has learned. The answers to the Vocabulary Crosswords can be found on pages 196 and 197.

Project Pages

Many of the projects and experiments in *Exploring Creation with Zoology 2* are "hands-on" and therefore cannot be preserved in a notebook. Each lesson in this notebooking journal provides a Project Page in which your student can write about what he did and learned from the various projects and experiments contained in the coursework. Be sure to take pictures of the finished products and glue them onto the Project Pages. Your child will enjoy looking back and remembering the fun he had learning zoology 2!

Cut and Fold Miniature Books

At the back of this journal, you will find Cut and Fold Miniature Book craft activities that correspond with the reading. These miniature books are designed to review the concepts learned in each lesson. Writing lines are provided on the miniature books so your students can record the information they have learned. Some books ask for specific information. Others do not and allow the students to record the facts they found most interesting. Students will cut out the pattern, write what they have learned in the designated places, then assemble the books according to the directions. Paste Pages are included in this journal for each miniature book activity. The Paste Pages provide a place for your students to preserve and display their Cut and Fold Miniature Books. Instructions are included for pasting the miniature books onto the Paste Pages.

These books are entirely optional. Some students thrive with the hands-on approach, while other students do not benefit academically from this type of activity. Allow your students to try the Cut and Fold Miniature Books to see if they enjoy learning in this way.

Dive Deeper

The Dive Deeper suggestions are designed to give your student additional ideas and activities that might enhance his studies such as: experiments, hands-on activities, research and living book titles, as well as audio and video resources. Because these assignments are entirely optional, they are not included in the suggested schedule for completing the notebooking journal.

Field Trip Sheets

Your family may wish to further enhance your studies by visiting a science museum, aquarium or perhaps Sea World. Field Trip Sheets are provided at the back of this notebooking journal to record your visits. You can make a pocket on the back of these sheets to hold any brochures or additional information you receive. Simply glue three edges (sides and bottom) of a half piece of construction paper to the bottom of the Field Trip Sheet.

Final Review

At the end of this journal are 50 questions that review the entire course. They can be answered orally or in writing. This is an optional activity; however, I believe your students would be pleasantly surprised to see how much they know about zoology 2 after answering the questions. The answers to the Final Review can be found on page 198.

Week	Day 1	Day 2
1	**Lesson 1 - Aquatic Animals** Read *T pp. 1-6* & Narrate Begin working on Fascinating Facts about Aquatic Animals *NJ p. 12* Read *T pp. 6-7* & Narrate Begin working on Fascinating Facts about the Ocean, Currents and Water *NJ p. 14-15*	Try This! *T p. 7* Read *T pp. 8-11* & Narrate Read *T pp. 12-15* & Narrate Try This! *T p. 15*
2	**Lesson 1 - Aquatic Animals** Read *T p. 16* & Narrate Written Narration: What Do You Remember? *T p. 16, NJ p. 16* Notebooking Activity: Draw the tides and regions of the ocean floor *T p. 17, NJ p. 17*	Ocean Box Project: Create an Ocean Box *T p. 17* Scripture Copywork *NJ p. 18* Vocabulary Crossword *NJ p. 20* Aquatic Animals Minibook *NJ Appendix p. A 7* Experiment: Water Temperature *T p. 18, NJ p. 25*
3	**Lesson 2 - Whales** Read *T pp. 19-21* & Narrate Begin working on Fascinating Facts about Whales *NJ p. 26* Read *T pp. 21-24* & Narrate	Read *T pp. 24-28* & Narrate Try This! *T p. 28* Read T pp. 29-32 & Narrate Try This! *T p. 32* Read *T pp. 32-36* & Narrate
4	**Lesson 2 - Whales** Read pp. 36-38 & Narrate Written Narration: What Do You Remember? *T p. 38, NJ p. 28* Notebooking Activity: Types of Whales *T p. 39, NJ p. 29* Notebooking Activity: Cetaceans Drawings *T p. 39, NJ p. 31* Notebooking Activity: Beached Whales Speech *T p. 39, NJ p. 33*	Ocean Box Project: Add whales to your ocean box *T p. 39* Scripture Copywork *NJ p. 34* Vocabulary Crossword *NJ p. 36* Whales Minibook *NJ Appendix p. A 13* Experiment: Sound Travel *T p. 39, NJ p. 41*
5	**Lesson 3 - Seals and Sea Cows** Read *T pp. 41-43* & Narrate Begin working on Fascinating Facts about Pinnipeds *NJ p. 42* Read *T pp. 44-47* & Narrate	Read *T pp. 47-50* & Narrate Read *T pp. 50-53* & Narrate
6	**Lesson 3 - Seals and Sea Cows** Written Narration: What Do You Remember? *T p. 53, NJ p. 43* Notebooking Activity: Sea Creatures *T p. 53, NJ p. 44* Notebooking Activity: Petting Manatees Essay *T p. 53, NJ p. 48*	Ocean Box Project: Add pinnipeds to your ocean box *T p. 53* Vocabulary Crossword *NJ p. 49* Scripture Copywork *NJ p. 50* Pinnipeds Minibooks *NJ Appendix A 17* Experiment: Blubber *T p. 54, NJ p. 55*
7	**Lesson 4 - Aquatic Herps** Read *T pp. 55-57* & Narrate Begin working on Fascinating Facts about Aquatic Herps *NJ p. 56* Try This! *T p. 57* Read *T pp. 58-61* & Narrate	Read *T pp. 61-62* & Narrate Try This! *T p. 62* Read *T pp. 63-67* & Narrate
8	**Lesson 4 - Aquatic Herps** Read *T pp. 67-71* & Narrate Written Narration: What Do You Remember? *T p. 71, NJ p. 57* Notebooking Activity: Sea Turtles Drawings *T p. 71, NJ p. 58* Notebooking Activity: Reptile Meets Amphibian Story *T p. 71, NJ p. 60* Notebooking Activity: Seat Turtle Preservation *T p. 71, NJ p. 61*	Ocean Box Project: Add a sea turtle and a sea snake to your ocean box *T p. 71* Scripture Copywork *NJ p. 62* Vocabulary Crossword *NJ p. 64* Herps Minibooks *NJ Appendix A 21* Experiment: Tadpole Growth *T p. 72, NJ p. 69*
9	**Lesson 5 - Primeval Reptiles** Read *T pp. 73-76* & Narrate Begin working on Fascinating Facts about Primeval Reptiles *NJ p. 70* Read *T pp. 76-78* & Narrate Try This! *T p. 78*	Read *T pp. 79-81* & Narrate Try This! *T p. 81* Read pp. 82-83 & Narrate Try This! *T p. 83*

Page numbers for the zoology text are indicated by *T p.* Page numbers for the notebooking journal are indicated by *NJ p.

Week	Day 1	Day 2
10	**Lesson 5 - Primeval Reptiles** Read ***T pp. 83-84*** & Narrate Written Narration: What Do You Remember? ***T p. 85, 71*** Notebooking Activity: Underwater Scene ***T p. 85, NJ p. 72*** Notebooking Activity: Marine Reptile Facts ***T p. 85, NJ p. 73*** Notebooking Activity: Leviathan Venn Diagram ***T p. 85, NJ p. 74***	Notebooking Activity: Leviathan Drawing ***T p. 85, NJ p. 75*** Scripture Copywork ***NJ p. 76*** Vocabulary Crossword ***NJ p. 78*** Primeval Reptiles Minibook ***NJ Appendix p. A 27*** Experiment: Fossil Sediment ***T p. 85, NJ p. 82***
11	**Lesson 6 - Fish** Read ***T pp. 87-90*** & Narrate Begin working on Fascinating Facts About Fish ***NJ p. 83*** Read ***T pp. 90-92*** & Narrate	Read ***T pp. 93-96*** & Narrate Read ***T pp. 96-98*** & Narrate
12	**Lesson 6 - Fish** Read pp. 98-100 & Narrate Written Narration: What Do You Remember? ***T p. 101, NJ p. 85*** Notebooking Activity: Label a Fish ***T p. 101, NJ p. 86*** Notebooking Activity: Fish Shapes ***T p. 101, NJ p. 87*** Notebooking Activity: Fish Design ***T p. 101, NJ p. 88*** Notebooking Activity: Lifecycle of a Salmon ***T p. 101, NJ p. 89***	Ocean Box Project: Add several kinds of fishes to your ocean box ***T p. 101*** Scripture Copywork ***NJ p. 90*** Vocabulary Crossword ***NJ p. 92*** Fish Minibook ***NJ Appendix p. A 31*** Experiment: Fish Temperature ***T p. 101, NJ p. 97***
13	**Lesson 7 - Sharks and Rays** Read ***T pp. 103-106*** & Narrate Begin working on Fascinating Facts about Sharks and Rays ***NJ p. 98*** Read ***T pp. 106-108*** & Narrate	Read ***T pp. 109-110*** & Narrate Try This! ***T p. 111*** Read ***T pp. 111-113*** & Narrate
14	**Lesson 7 - Sharks and Rays** Read ***T pp. 114-118*** & Narrate Written Narration: What Do You Remember? ***T p. 119, NJ p. 100*** Notebooking Activity: Sharks & Rays Illustrations ***T p. 119, NJ p. 101*** Notebooking Activity: Lamprey & Hagfish Illustrations ***T p. 119, NJ p. 102***	Notebooking Activity: Shark Bites Speech ***T p. 119, NJ p. 103*** Ocean Box Project: Add a shark and ray to your ocean box ***T p. 119*** Scripture Copywork ***NJ p. 104*** Vocabulary Crossword ***NJ p. 106*** Sharks and Rays Minibooks ***NJ Appendix p. A 37*** Experiment: Electricity in Salt Water ***T p. 119, NJ p. 111***
15	**Lesson 8 - Crustaceans** Read ***T pp. 121-123*** & Narrate Begin working on Fascinating Facts about Crustaceans ***NJ p. 112*** Read ***T pp. 123-126*** & Narrate	Read ***T pp. 126-130*** & Narrate Read ***T pp. 130-134*** & Narrate Read ***T pp. 135-137*** & Narrate Try This! ***T p. 137***
16	**Lesson 8 - Crustaceans** Read ***T p. 138*** & Narrate Written Narration: What Do You Remember? ***T p. 138, NJ p. 115*** Notebooking Activity: Crustacean & Crab Ilustration ***T p. 138, NJ p. 116*** Notebooking Activity: Crab Conversation ***T p. 138, NJ p. 117***	Project: Animal Quiz Game ***T p. 139*** Ocean Box Project: Add crustaceans to your ocean box ***T p. 140*** Scripture Copywork ***NJ p. 118*** Vocabulary Crossword ***NJ p. 120*** Crustaceans Minibooks ***NJ Appendix p. A 45*** Experiment: Raise Sea Monkeys or Triops ***T p. 140***
17	**Lesson 9 - Mollusks** Read ***T pp. 141-143*** & Narrate Begin working on Fascinating Facts about Mollusks ***NJ p. 125*** Read ***T pp. 143-146*** & Narrate	Read ***T pp. 146-151*** & Narrate Read ***T pp. 151-153*** & Narrate

***Page numbers for the zoology text are indicated by *T p*. Page numbers for the notebooking journal are indicated by *NJ p*.**

Week	Day 1	Day 2
18	**Lesson 9 - Mollusks** Read ***T pp. 154-156*** & Narrate Written Narration: What Do You Remember? ***T p. 156, NJ p. 127*** Notebooking Activity: Bivalves and Gastropods Illustrations ***T p. 156, NJ p. 128*** Ocean Box Project: Add some mollusks to your ocean box ***T p. 157***	Scripture Copywork ***NJ p. 130*** Vocabulary Crossword ***NJ p. 132*** Mollusks Minibooks ***NJ Appendix A 47*** Experiment: Resonance ***T p. 157, NJ p. 137*** Project: Make a Conchology Box ***T p. 158, NJ p. 136***
19	**Lesson 10 - Cephalopods** Read ***T pp. 159-161*** & Narrate Begin working on Fascinating Facts about Cephalopods ***NJ p. 138*** Read ***T pp. 162-164*** & Narrate	Read ***T pp. 164-168*** & Narrate Try This! ***T p. 168***
20	**Lesson 10 - Cephalopods** Read ***T pp. 168-170*** & Narrate Written Narration: What Do You Remember? ***T p. 170, NJ p. 139*** Notebooking Activity: Cephalopod Drawing ***T p. 171, NJ p. 140*** Notebooking Activity: Sperm Whale Story ***T p. 171, NJ p. 143***	Ocean Box Project: Add some cephalopods to your ocean box ***T p. 171*** Scripture Copywork ***NJ p. 144*** Vocabulary Crossword ***NJ p. 146*** Cephalopods Minibook ***NJ Appendix A 51*** Experiment: Buoyancy ***T p. 171, NJ p. 151***
21	**Lesson 11 - Echinoderms** Read ***T pp. 173-175*** & Narrate Begin working on Fascinating Facts about Echinoderms ***NJ p. 152*** Read ***T pp. 176-177*** & Narrate	Read ***T pp. 177-180*** & Narrate Read ***T pp. 180-182*** & Narrate
22	**Lesson 11 - Echinoderms** Written Narration: What Do You Remember? ***T p. 182, NJ p. 154*** Notebooking Activity: Echinoderms ***T p. 183, NJ p. 155*** Notebooking Activity: Animal Pages ***T p. 183, NJ p. 156*** Notebooking Activity: Legend of the Sand Dollar ***T p. 183, NJ p. 159***	Ocean Box Project: Add some echinoderms to your ocean box ***T p. 184*** Scripture Copywork ***NJ p. 160*** Vocabulary Crossword ***NJ p. 162*** Echinoderms Minibook ***NJ Appendix A 55*** Project: Salty Brittle Stars ***T p. 184, NJ p. 166***
23	**Lesson 12 - Cnidarians** Read ***T pp. 185-187*** & Narrate Begin working on Fascinating Facts about Cnidarians ***NJ p. 167*** Read ***T pp. 188-191*** & Narrate	Read ***T pp. 191-194*** & Narrate Read ***T pp. 194-197*** & Narrate
24	**Lesson 12 - Cnidarians** Read ***T pp. 198-199*** & Narrate Written Narration: What Do You Remember? ***T p. 199, NJ p. 168*** Notebooking Activity: Animal Pages ***T p. 199, NJ p. 169*** Notebooking Activity: Great Barrier Reef ***T p. 199, NJ p. 171***	Ocean Box Project: Add cnidarians to your ocean box ***T p. 200*** Scripture Copywork ***NJ p. 172*** Vocabulary Crossword, ***NJ p. 174*** Cnidarians Minibook ***NJ Appendix p. A 59*** Experiment: Currents ***T p. 200, NJ p. 179***
25	**Lesson 13 - Other Interesting Aquatic Animals** Read ***T pp. 201-203*** & Narrate Begin working on Fascinating Facts about Other Aquatic Animals ***NJ p. 180*** Read ***T pp. 203-206*** & Narrate	Read ***T pp. 206-208*** & Narrate Try This! ***T p. 208*** Read ***T pp. 209-212*** & Narrate
26	**Lesson 13 - Other Interesting Aquatic Animals** Read ***T pp. 212-216*** & Narrate Written Narration: What Do You Remember? ***T p. 216, NJ p. 182*** Notebooking Activity: Animal Pages ***NJ p. 183***	Ocean Box Project: Add sponges and worms to your ocean box ***T p. 217*** Scripture Copywork ***NJ p. 186*** Vocabulary Crossword ***NJ p. 188*** Interesting Aquatic Animals Minibook ***NJ Appendix p. A 61*** Experiment: Desalination ***T p. 217, NJ p. 193***

Page numbers for the zoology text are indicated by *T p.* Page numbers for the notebooking journal are indicated by *NJ p.

This journal belongs to:

____

Fascinating Facts about AQUATIC ANIMALS

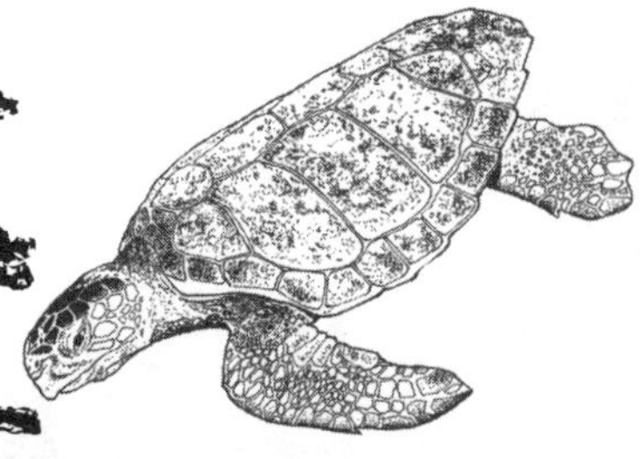

Lesson 1

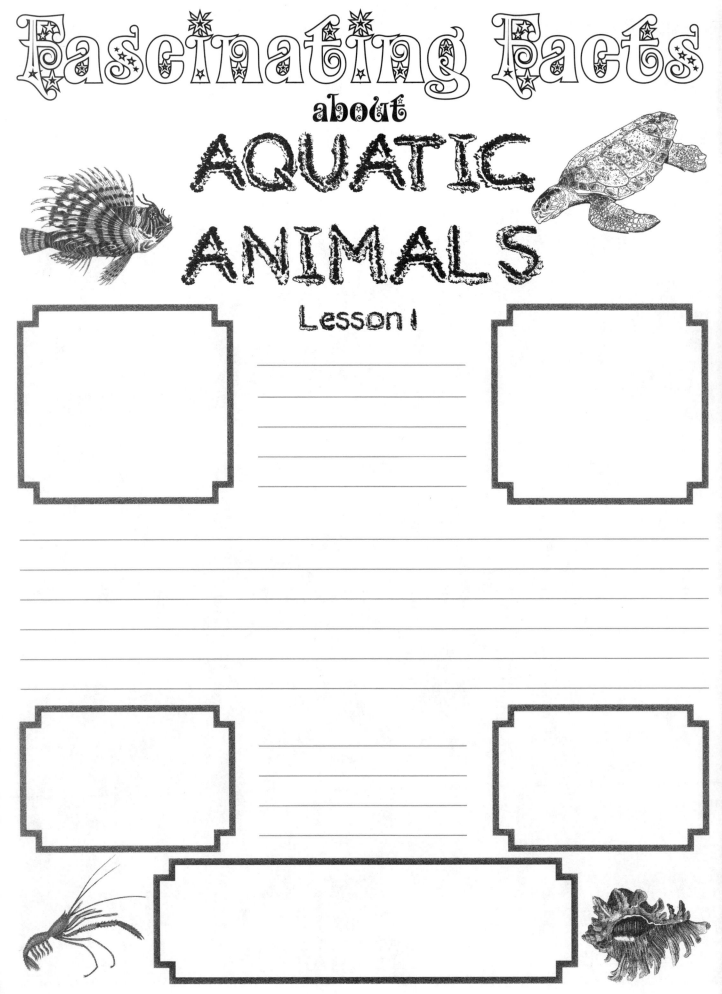

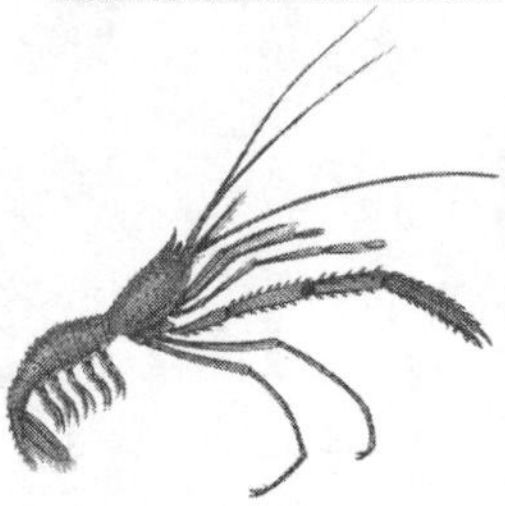

Fascinating Facts about AQUATIC ANIMALS

Lesson 1

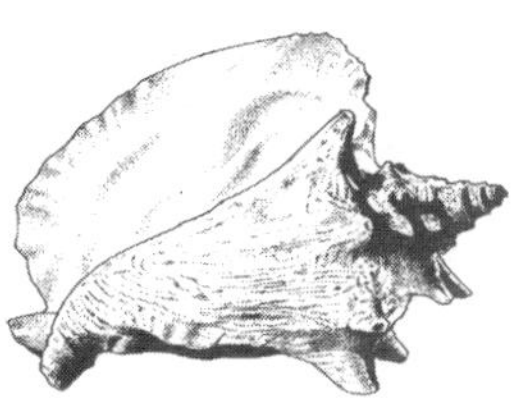

Fascinating Facts about CURRENTS & WATER

Lesson 1

SURFACE CURRENTS

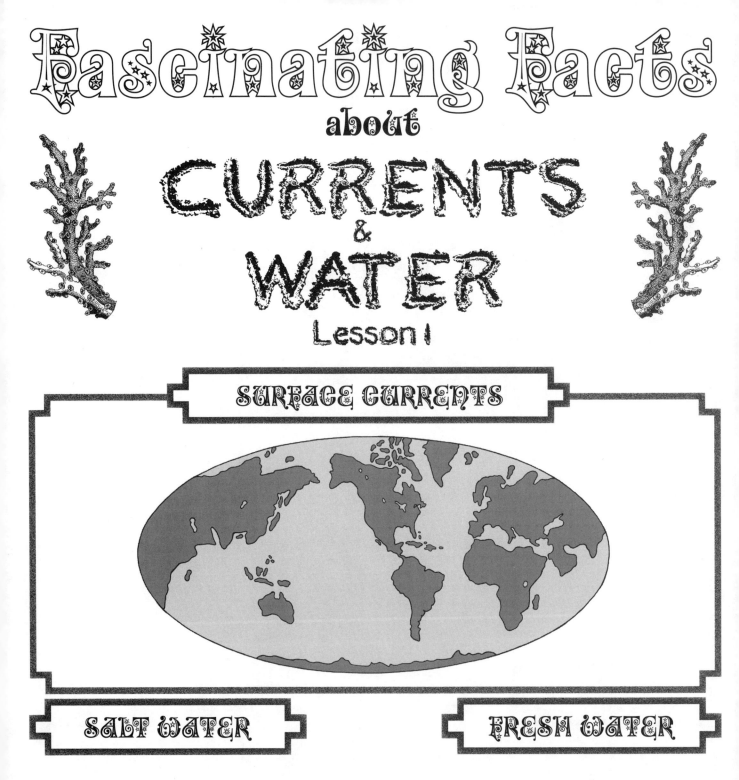

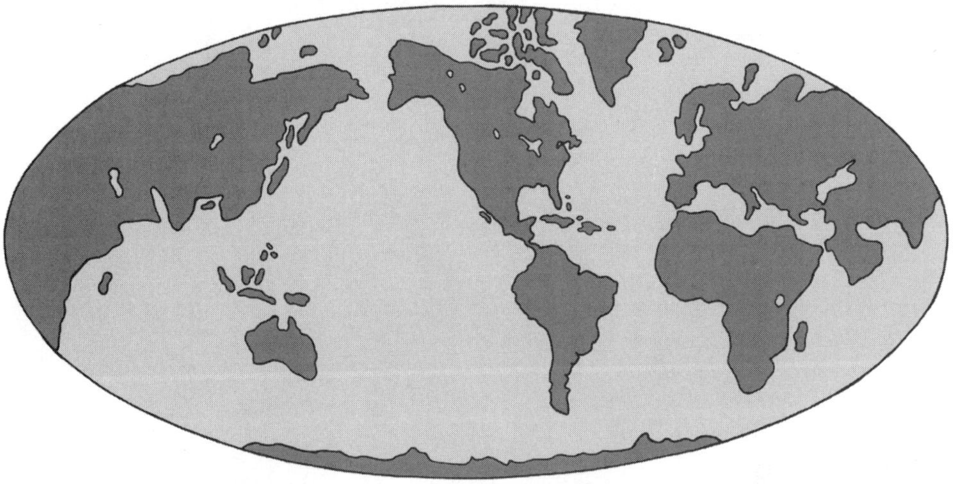

SALT WATER

FRESH WATER

Fascinating Facts about the Ocean

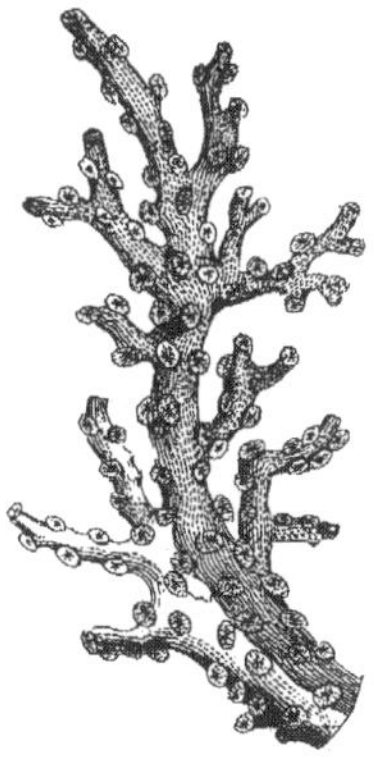

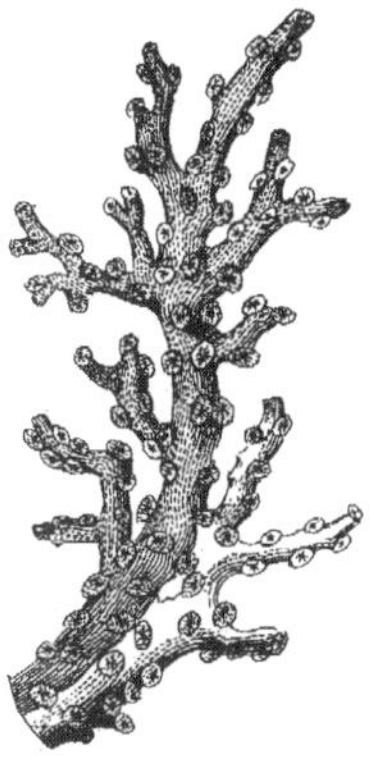

Lesson 1

Zones

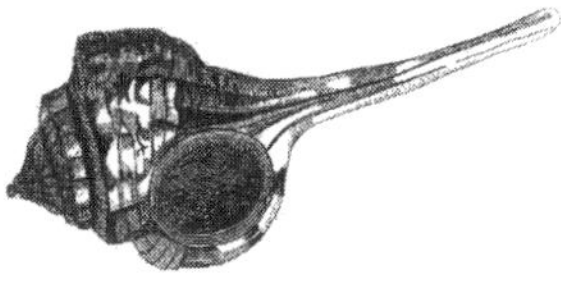

Abyssal Animals

Name ______________________________ Date ______________

What Do You Remember? Lesson 1 Review Questions

1. What are nektonic creatures?

2. What are benthic creatures?

3. What are plankton?

4. Where can zooplankton be found at night?

5. Why are plankton important to all sea life?

6. What are filter feeders?

7. Can you name the five oceans in the world?

8. What are seas?

9. What are estuaries?

10. Beginning from the shore out to the deep, what are the four zones of the ocean floor?

11. From the surface of the ocean to the deep, what are the three zones in which aquatic creatures live?

12. What are the circular currents called?

13. What are the currents caused by temperature and salt levels called?

14. What causes the tides?

What Causes the Tides

Regions of the Ocean Floor

COPYWORK

Praise the LORD from the earth, you great sea creatures and all ocean depths.

Psalm 148:7

COPYWORK

Praise the LORD from the earth, you great sea creatures and all ocean depths.

Psalm 148:7

Vocabulary Crossword

Lesson 1

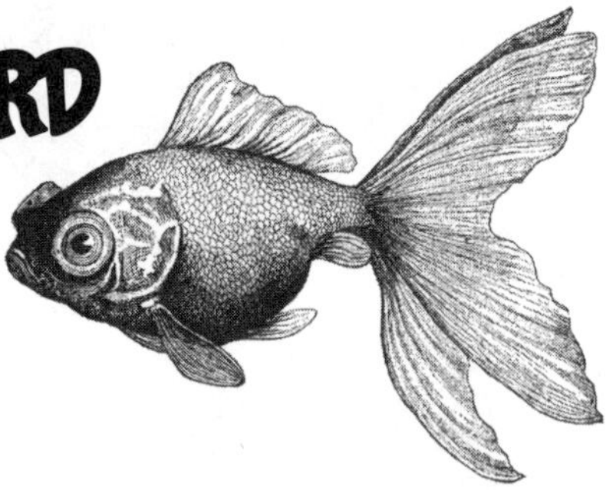

NEKTONIC
BENTHIC
PLANKTON
MAMMALS
MIDNIGHT ZONE
CONTINENTAL SLOPE
CONTINENTAL RISE
THERMOHALINE CURRENTS

REPTILES
HIGH TIDE
SUNLIT ZONE
AMPHIBIANS
INVERTEBRATE
BIOLUMINESCENCE
SPRING TIDES
FISHES

LOW TIDE
BRACKISH
TWILIGHT ZONE
ZOOPLANKTON
CONTINENTAL SHELF
ABYSSAL PLAIN
VERTEBRATE
NEAP TIDES

GYRES
ESTUARY
SEA
SESSILE

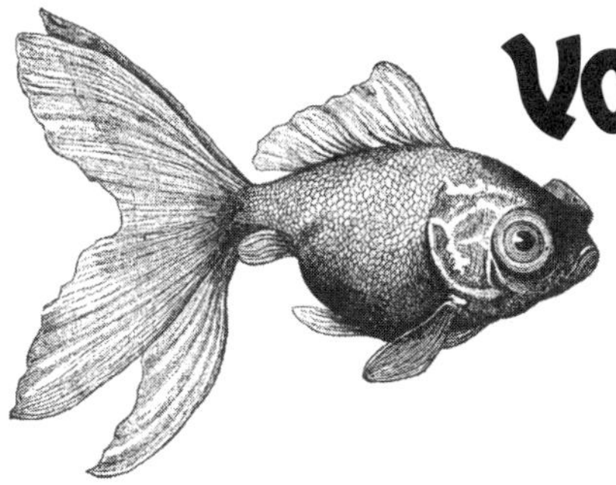

Vocabulary Crossword

Lesson 1

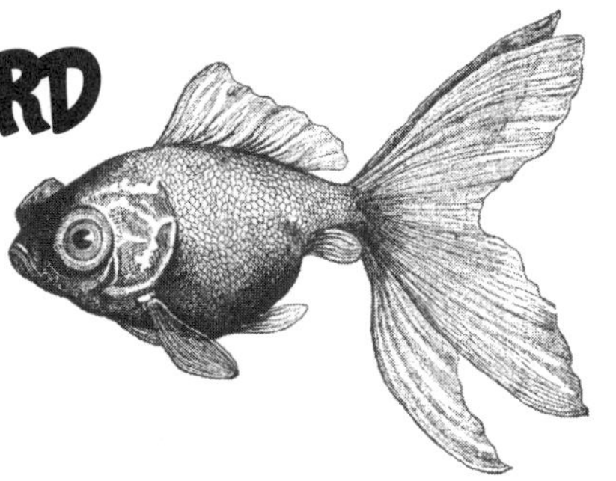

Across

1. These creatures are like reptiles, but they don't have scales.
7. Animals that are cold-blooded and have a backbone, but don't breathe air.
10. Deep currents in the ocean resulting from water evaporating from the surface of the ocean. TWO WORDS
11. Organisms that drift or float in the water because they cannot swim strongly enough to move against the ocean current.
12. Animals that don't swim, but scurry, crawl, hop, scoot, burrow, or slither across the bottom of a body of water. They are also called the benthos.
13. An animal that has a backbone.
15. The area that begins before the bottom of the ocean floor, where it is darker than midnight. No light from the sun ever reaches down this deep into the ocean. TWO WORDS
17. One part near the very end of the continental slope drop off, where the slope becomes much more gentle. TWO WORDS
19. The place where a river meets with an ocean or sea.
24. The part of the continent that is underwater. It slopes gradually downward, and the water gets deeper and deeper. TWO WORDS
25. An animal that doesn't have a backbone.
26. A body of water that is smaller than an ocean. It is made up of salt water because it is connected to an ocean.
27. Tides that occur when the sun's gravity works against the moon's gravity, causing the high tides to become lower and the low tides to become higher. TWO WORDS
28. The part of the ocean that is well lit by the sun. TWO WORDS

Down

2. Warm-blooded creatures that breathe air and give birth to live young that drink milk from their mother's body. They also have a backbone and hair.
3. What we call it when the ocean's water comes way up onto the shore. TWO WORDS
4. What we call animals that can get from one place to another by propelling, gliding, or paddling through the water.
5. The area deeper down the continental slope where it is fairly dark with very little sunlight coming through. TWO WORDS
6. A giant cliff-like drop-off at the end of the continental shelf in the ocean. TWO WORDS
8. Tides that are caused by the sun working with the moon to pull on the oceans of the world, causing the high tide to become higher than usual and the low tide to become lower than usual. TWO WORDS
9. Cold-blooded creatures that have scales, breathe air, lay eggs and have a backbone.
14. What we call it when a creature has the ability to make its own light, much like a firefly.
16. The deep, dark ocean floor, located at the end of the continental rise. TWO WORDS
18. Animals that stick themselves to one place and do not move around.
20. What we call it when the ocean's water pulls way back, sometimes exposing a lot of the beach. TWO WORDS
21. A certain type of plankton that are a lot like animals because they need to eat to get food.
22. Water that is less salty than seawater but saltier than fresh water.
23. Circular patterns formed by the surface currents in the world's oceans.

Aquatic Animals & the Ocean Minibook

Lesson 1

Paste your Aquatic Animals
and the Ocean Tab Book onto
this page.

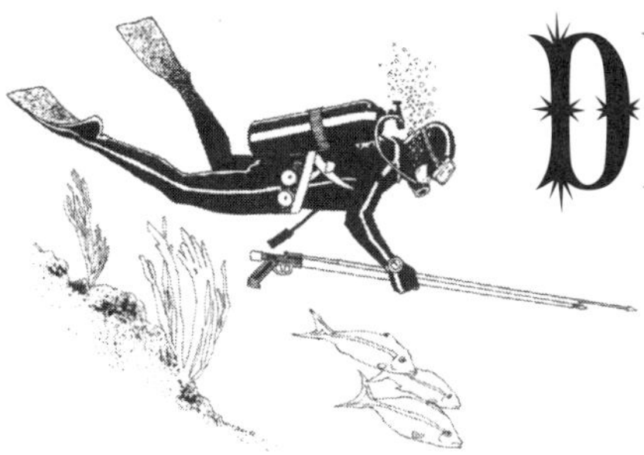

DIVE DEEPER

Lesson 1

Create Abyssal Animals

You can create some abyssal animals for your ocean box. Find images on the Internet, or look for them in the books or DVDs below to see what they look like.

Why Don't Oceans Freeze?

Have you ever wondered why rivers and lakes freeze in the winter, but oceans do not? Let's do an experiment to see why.

You will need:
1 gallon freezer bag
Crushed ice
1 cup of salt
A thermometer

Fill the gallon freezer bag half way with crushed ice and water. Measure the temperature and record it. Add salt and seal the bag. Place the bag on the counter and allow the ice to melt for 1 hour. Check the temperature again. The temperature should be less than 32 degrees Fahrenheit. Even though the temperature is below freezing, the ice continues to melt. This is because the salt lowered the freezing point of the water. The water will not freeze unless it reaches a much colder temperature than 32 degrees. This is why water in the ocean rarely freezes. The salt keeps the ocean water from freezing. Occasionally, the top layer of the water, which has less salt, will freeze, while the bottom will not. This enables ocean animals to live all year long in their watery world.

Create a Model of the Ocean Floor

Using the salt dough recipe below, you can create a model of the ocean floor.

Ingredients:
4 cups flour
1 cup salt
1 1/2 cups hot water (tap water)
2 teaspoons vegetable oil (optional)
Food coloring

Mix the ingredients together. You may want to add this to your ocean box.

Book and DVD Suggestions

The Deep: The Extraordinary Creatures of the Abyss by Claire Nouvian. This picture book contains the strange, beautiful, grotesque and wonderful creatures that inhabit the abyss. Artistically presented.
Down, Down, Down: A Journey to the Bottom of the Sea by Steven Jenkins. A top to bottom look at the ocean.
IMAX Deep Sea (DVD) narrated by Johnny Depp and Kate Winslet. This stunning film is an exploration of the world beneath the sea and its bizarre and exotic inhabitants.

*Be aware that some titles may contain evolutionary content

My Aquatic Animals Project

Lesson 1

What I did:

What I did:

What I learned:

What I learned:

Scientific Speculation Sheet

Water Temperature

Lesson 1

Name______________________________ Date _______________

Materials Used:

Procedure:

Hypothesis:

Results:

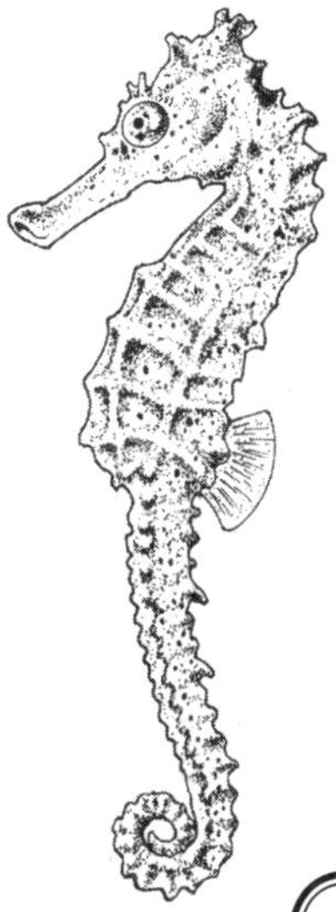

Fascinating Facts about WHALES

Lesson 2

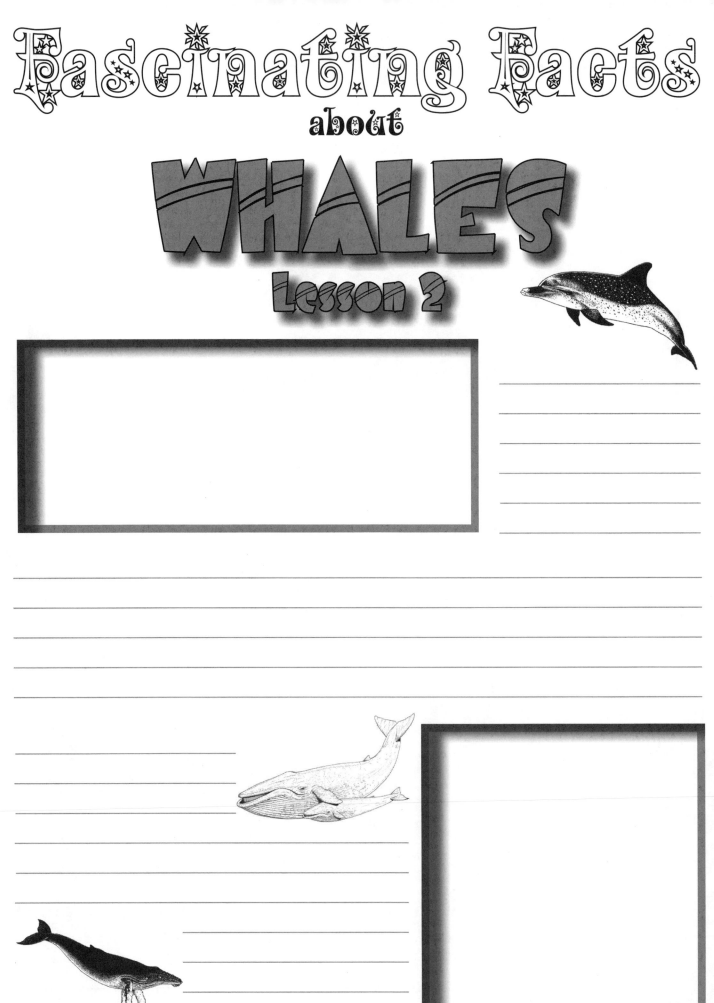

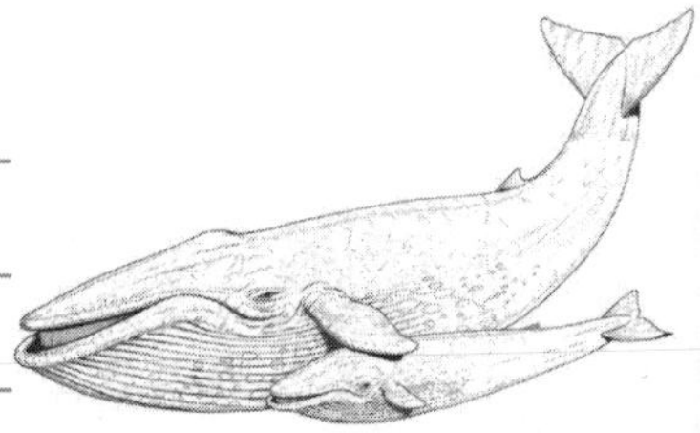

Fascinating Facts
about
WHALES
Lesson 2

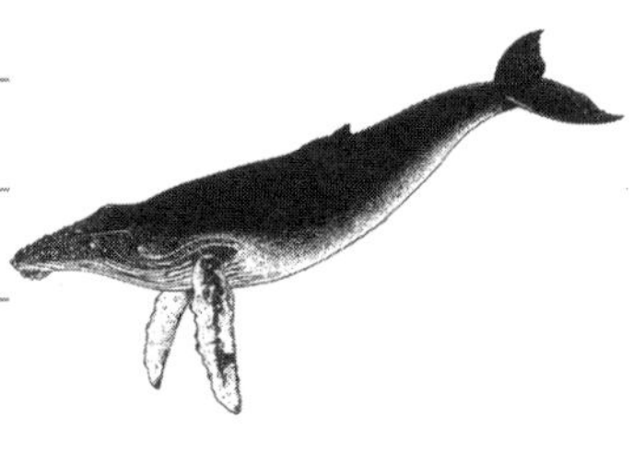

Name ______________________________ Date ______________

What Do You Remember?
Lesson 2 Review Questions

1. How does a cetacean move its tail to propel itself through the water?

2. Which is the most important sense for a whale: smelling, hearing, or seeing?

3. What must a calf do as soon as it is born?

4. How does the mother help it do this?

5. Why must a whale have a blowhole?

6. Where do most whales spend the summer and winter? Why?

7. What is breaching?

8. What is lobtailing?

9. What is spyhopping?

10. What is logging?

11. Why did whalers want to kill whales?

12. Which two kinds of whales did whalers really like?

13. How are toothed whales different from baleen whales?

14. What kind of whale has a "horn" like a unicorn?

15. Name a difference between dolphins and porpoises.

16. What is the largest animal on earth?

Toothed Whales

Baleen Whales

Whale Migration

Whale Behavior

Cetaceans

Lesson 2

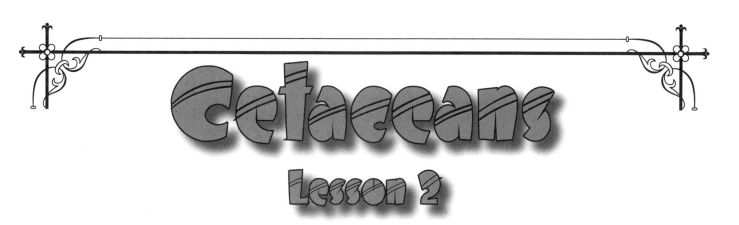

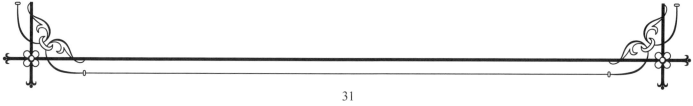

Cetaceans

Lesson 2

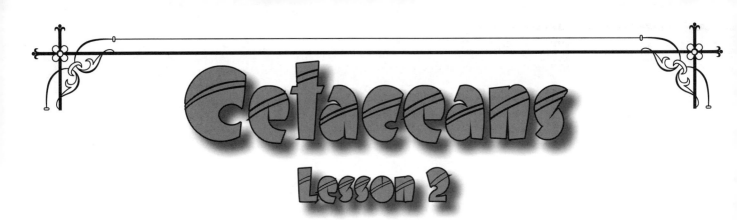

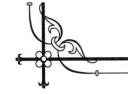

Beached Whales Speech

Lesson 2

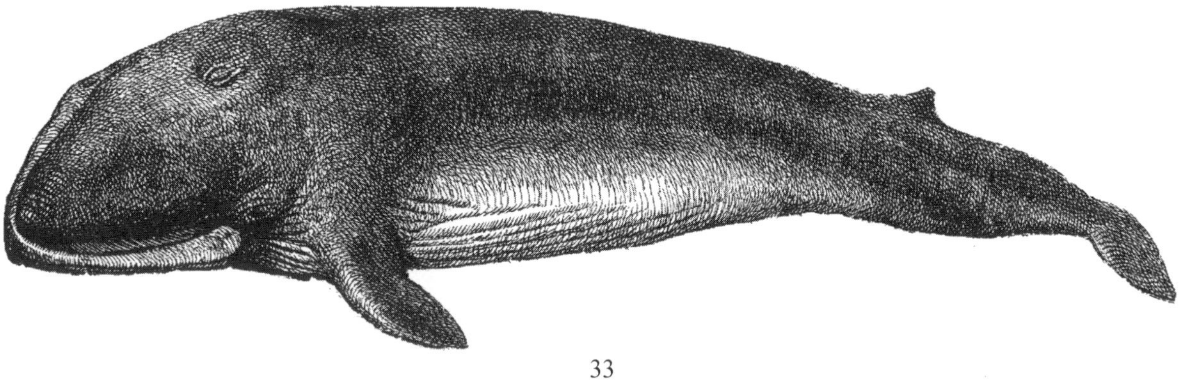

COPYWORK

For as Jonas was three days and three nights in the whale's belly; so shall the Son of man be three days and three nights in the heart of the earth.

Matthew 12:40

COPYWORK

For as Jonas was three days and three nights in the whale's belly; so shall the Son of man be three days and three nights in the heart of the earth.

Matthew 12:40

Vocabulary Crossword

Lesson 2

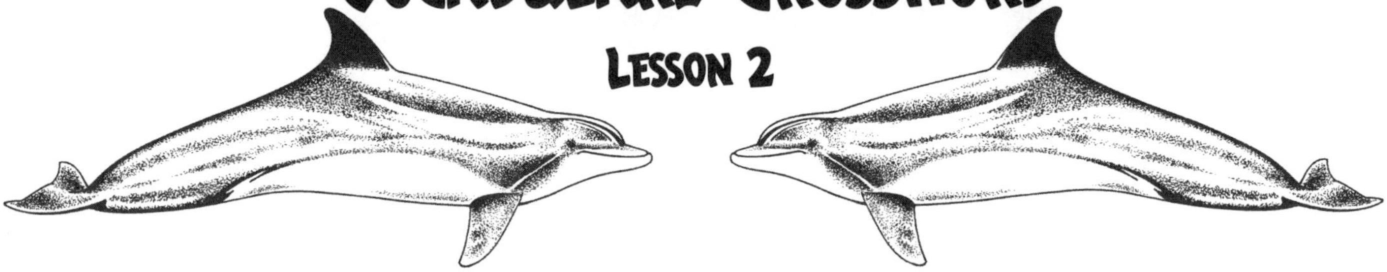

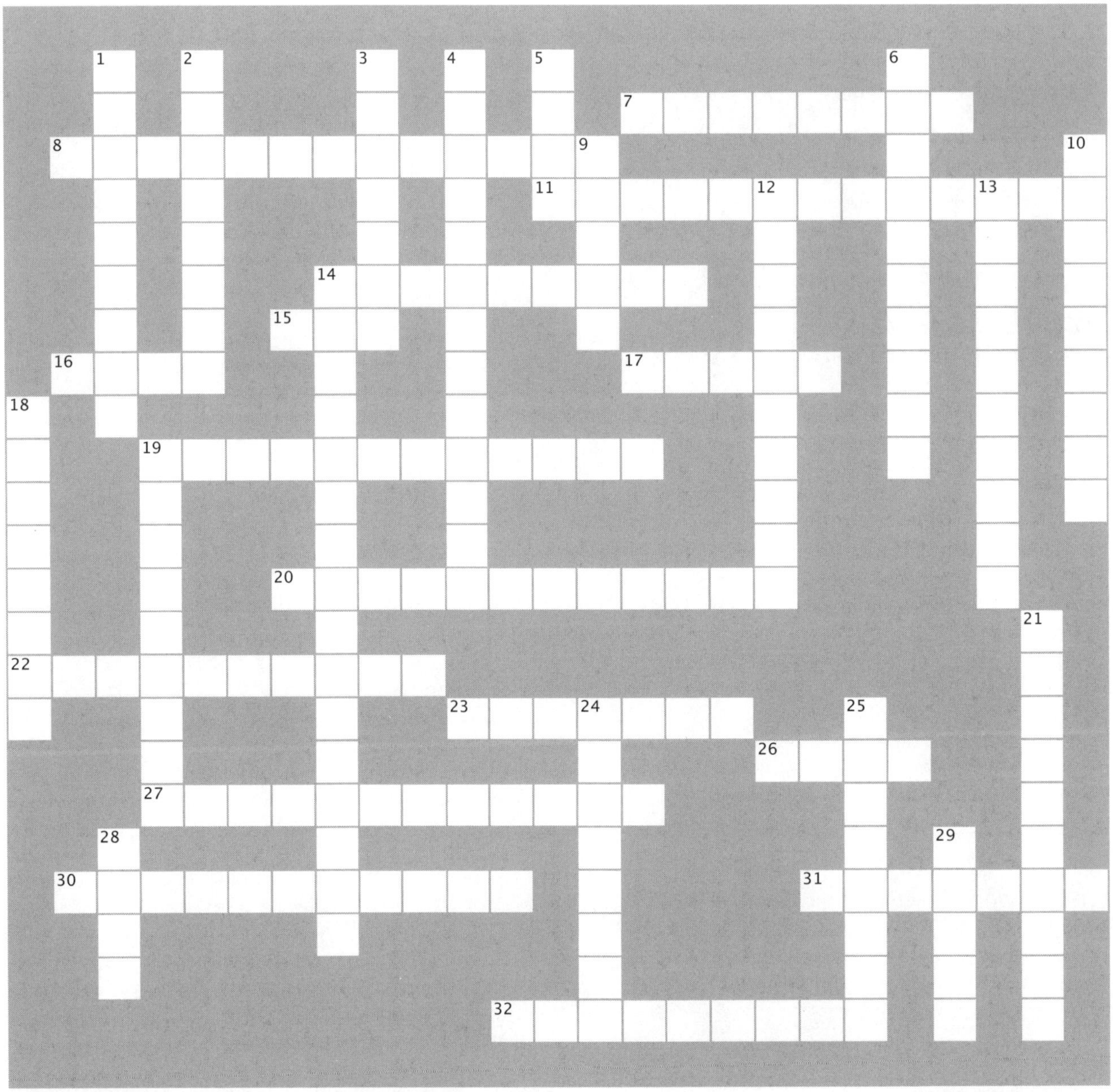

BLUE WHALE
MARINE MAMMALS
ANIMALIA
CHORDATA
MAMMALIA
BALEEN WHALES
TOOTHED WHALES
PORPOISE
HUMPBACK WHALE

BLOWHOLE
ESOPHAGUS
BEACHED
LOBTAILING
CONSERVATION LAWS
HERD
ECHOLOCATION
SEA CANARY
BELUGA WHALE

TRACHEA
EPIGLOTTIS
SPYHOPPING
WHALERS
POD
CALF
VIVIPAROUS
SONAR
BACHELOR PODS

KRILL
ORCA
RIGHT WHALE
GRAY WHALE
MOLT
FLUKE
CETACEANS

Vocabulary Crossword

Lesson 2

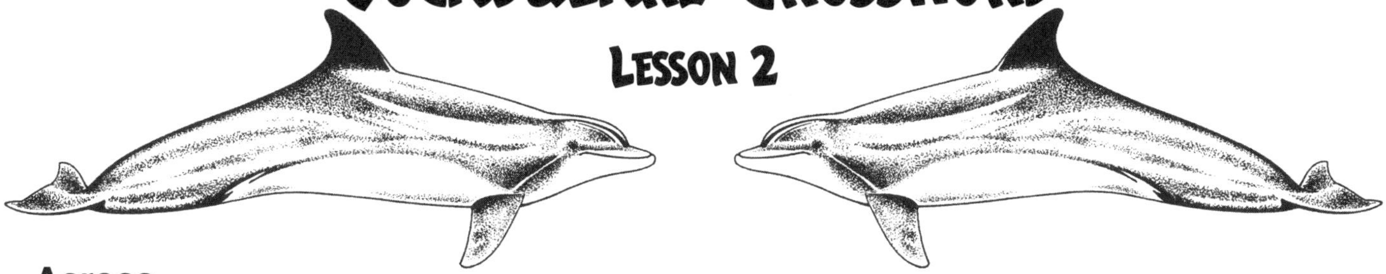

Across

7. The class in which mammals are placed.
8. Mammals that live in the ocean. TWO WORDS
11. These cetaceans have teeth. TWO WORDS
14. What we call whales.
15. A group of whales.
16. A certain kind of whale with specific markings. It is also known as a killer whale.
17. A very tiny, shrimp-like zooplankton.
19. These cetaceans have no teeth. Instead they have long strips of bristled plates that hang from their upper mouths. TWO WORDS
20. Groups of all-male whales. TWO WORDS
22. What we call it when a whale sits straight up in the water with its head positioned out of the water.
23. The tube at the end of the throat that leads to the lungs.
26. A whale's young.
27. The process in which a whale uses its God-made sonar to "see" in the water.
30. A beautiful, white whale that looks almost like a large dolphin and resides mostly in the cold waters off the coast of Alaska. TWO WORDS
31. Fishermen that hunted whales.
32. A type of whale that congregates in huge numbers off the coast of California. TWO WORDS

Down

1. Another name for a Beluga whale. TWO WORDS
2. The kingdom in which all animals are placed.
3. What we call it when a whale gets stranded on the beach.
4. A type of whale that is easy to identify because of its warty looking bumps found on the top of its head. TWO WORDS
5. When a whale's outer layer of skin peels off, revealing a new skin.
6. A type of whale that was a major target for whalers. TWO WORDS
9. The name of the system that allows whales to echolocate.
10. The tube at the end of the throat that leads to the stomach.
12. The small flap that covers the trachea, keeping food and liquid from entering the lungs when drinking or eating.
13. This is when a whale faces downward in the water with only its fluke sticking out, splashing the water with a thunderous splash.
14. Laws that help save creatures. TWO WORDS
18. A creature that is different from a dolphin because it is shorter, wider, has no beak, and has a different dorsal fin.
19. The largest of God's creatures. TWO WORDS
21. Animals that give birth to live young are called____________ animals.
24. The order in which animals with backbones are placed.
25. The "nose" on top of a whale's head that the whale uses to breathe and produce sound.
28. An extremely large pod.
29. The end of a whale's tail, which it uses for steering and power when swimming.

Whales Minibook
Lesson 2

Paste your Whales Layered
Book onto this page.

DIVE DEEPER

Lesson 2

How Big are Whales?

Using the key below, explore and experience the actual size of the whales about which you learned. Using a ball of yarn, measure out these sizes in a large outdoor area – a park, big yard or empty street. Label each whale. You'll be amazed at their sizes!

Beluga: 15 feet
Blue: 110 feet (only do this one if you have a huge space)
Bowhead: 60 feet
Sperm: 60 feet
Gray: 45 feet
Killer: 27 feet
Pilot: 20 feet

Create a Whale Mobile

You can create a mobile using a coat hanger and pictures of the different types of whales.

You will need:
Different whale pictures printed from the Internet (or you can draw your own)
String, cut into different lengths
Glue
A coat hanger
White computer paper
A hole punch

Cut out the pictures of the whales. Glue a sheet of paper to the back of each whale and write down information you learned about them. Punch a hole at the top of the whales and tie a piece of string around each one. Make sure your strings are different lengths. Now tie each whale to the coat hanger and hang your mobile.

Book and DVD Suggestions

Whale Passing by Eve Bunting. Father and Daughter watch as whales pass on their migratory journeys.
Baby Beluga (Raffi Songs to Read) by Raffi. Children will become acquainted with enchanting Baby Beluga.
Amos and Boris by William Steig. Not a true whale book, but a fun story about the friendship between a whale and a mouse – a twist of the Aesop fable *The Lion and the Mouse*.
Humphrey the Lost Whale by Wendy Tokuda. A whale who mistakenly entered the San Francisco Bay.
Big Blue Whale: Read and Wonder by Nicola Davies. A look at the largest mammal ever to inhabit the earth.
Moby Dick by Herman Melville. An American classic.
Danny and Daisy: A Tale of a Dolphin Duo by Suzanne Tate. Helpful humans rescue two young dolphins and take them to a science center for rehabilitation.
Katie K. Whale: A Whale of a Tale by Suzanne Tate. A tale based on the true story of a killer whale.
The Snail and the Whale by Julia Donaldson. A story of a beached whale.
Whales: An Unforgettable Journey (DVD) narrated by Patrick Stewart. Follow humpbacks, orcas, right whales and dolphins for a stunning new perspective on these mysterious marine mammoths.
Free Willy (DVD)**.** An adventure you'll never forget about a 12 yr. old boy and a three ton killer whale.

*Be aware that some titles may contain evolutionary content

My Whale Projects
Lesson 2

What I did:

What I did:

What I learned:

What I learned:

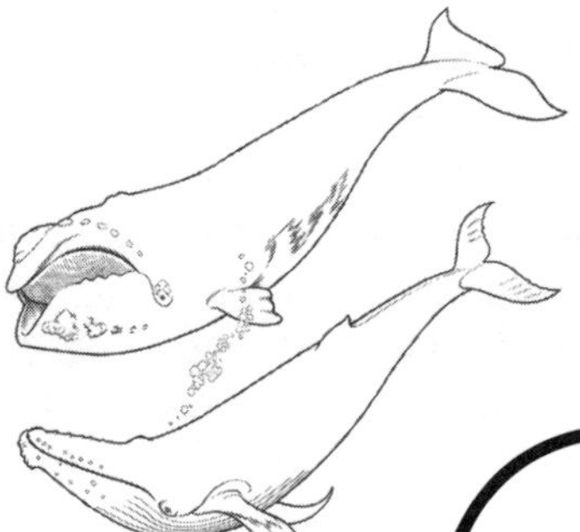

Scientific Speculation Sheet

Sound Travel

Lesson 2

Name___________________________ Date ______________

Materials Used:

Procedure:

Hypothesis:

Results:

Fascinating Facts about Pinnipeds

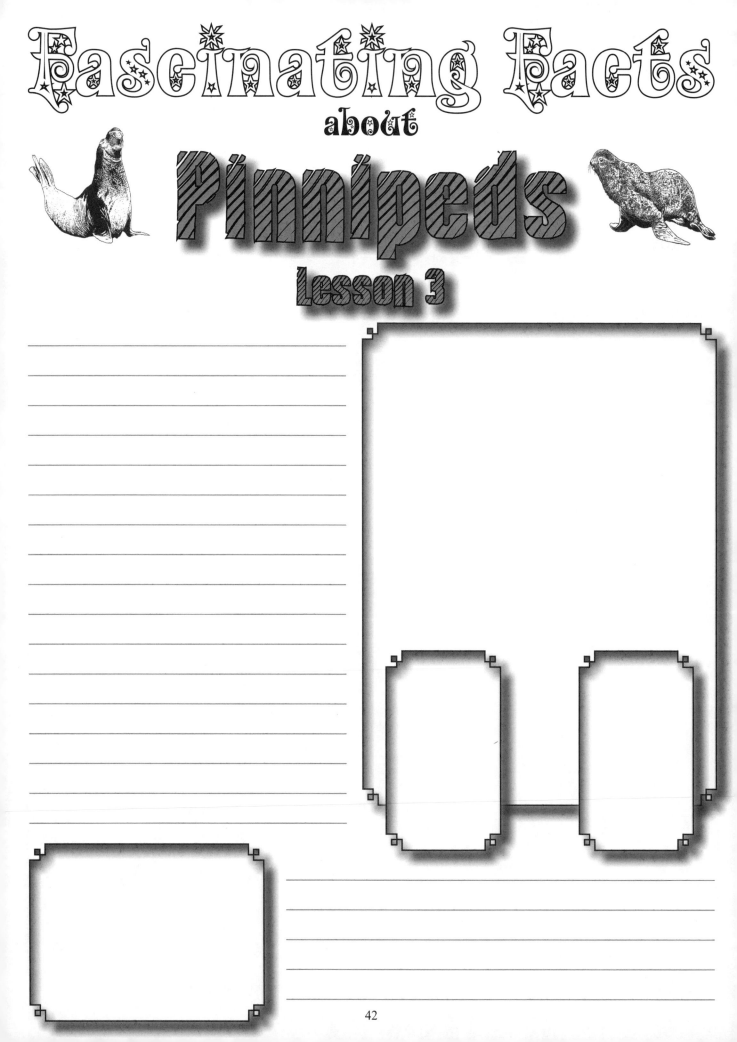

Lesson 3

Name ______________________________ Date ______________

What Do You Remember? Lesson 3 Review Questions

1. What is the main difference between a true seal and a sea lion?

2. What are the differences between a fur seal and a sea lion?

3. What is a haul out?

4. What is a rookery?

5. What are some dangers to pinnipeds?

6. How does a walrus differ from other pinnipeds?

7. What does the walrus family name, Odobenidae, mean?

8. What is the main difference between a manatee and a dugong?

9. What temperature of water do manatees like?

10. What do manatees do when they meet one another?

11. Why do manatees need to stay in shallow water?

12. Why is this dangerous for them?

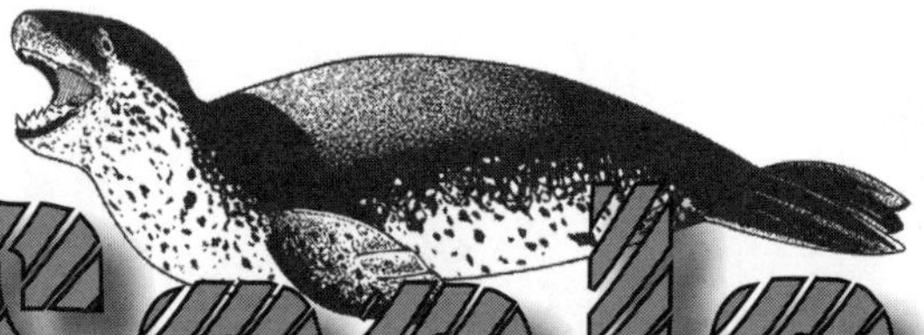

True Seals

Sea Lions

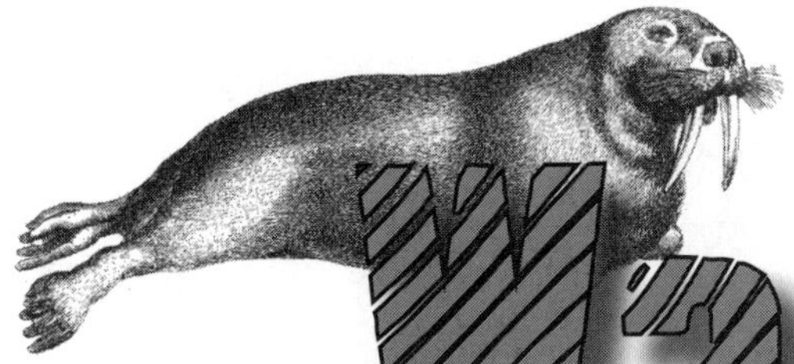

Walruses

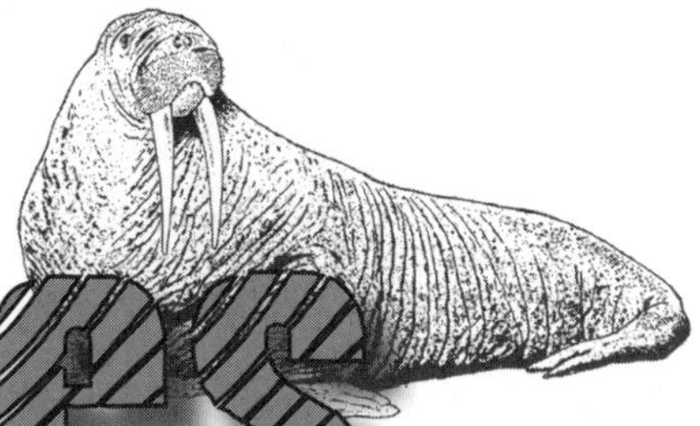

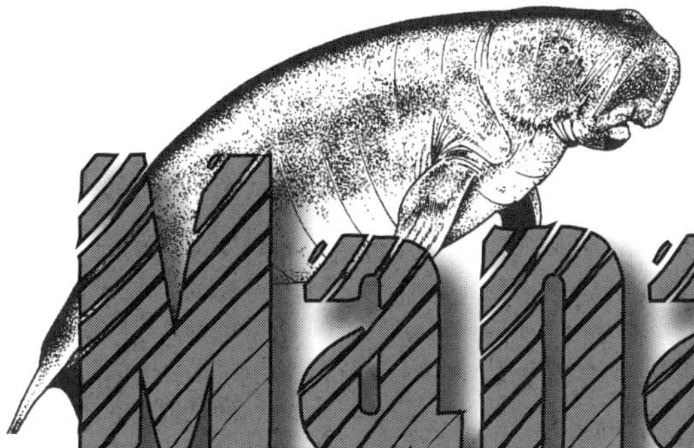

Manatees

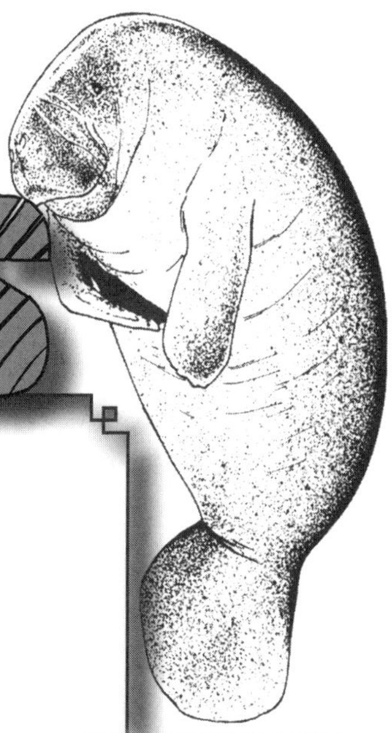

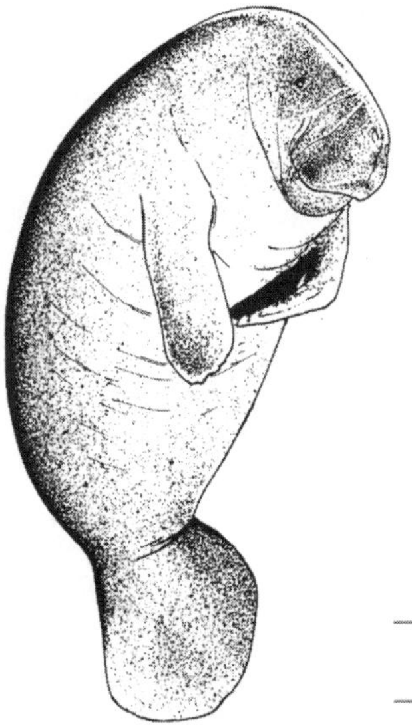

Petting Manatees
Lesson 3

Vocabulary Crossword

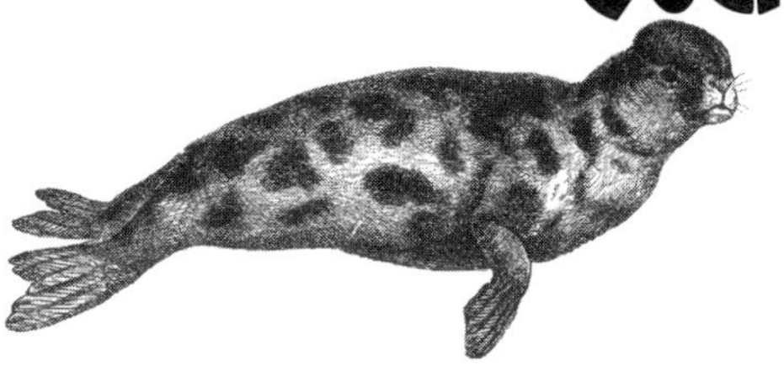

Lesson 3

SEA LION
PUPS
MANATEE
PINNIPEDS
HAUL OUT
ROOKERIES
BULLS
COWS
WEANED
EARED SEALS
ODOBENIDAE
TUSKS
SIRENIA
PHOCIDAE

Across

3. The family that seals belong in, coming from the Greek word that means "seal."
4. A mammal in the order Sirenia, sometimes called a sea cow.
6. Another name for pinnipeds with ear-flaps. TWO WORDS
10. Male pinnipeds.
11. When a baby no longer needs to eat by nursing we say it has been ________.
13. The extra long teeth protruding from a walrus's mouth.

Down

1. When pinnipeds come ashore, hauling their big bodies out of the water. TWO WORDS
2. Manatees belong in this order.
3. Mammals that belong to the order Pinnipedia, including seals, sea lions, walruses and manatees.
5. The family in which walruses belong.
7. The name of the breeding grounds for pinnipeds.
8. A large, dog-like creature that can be found from San Diego to Alaska and in the cooler areas of Australia and New Zealand. TWO WORDS
9. What we call baby sea lions.
12. Female pinnipeds.

COPYWORK

Then I heard every creature in heaven
and on earth and under the earth and
on the sea, and all that is in them,
singing: "To him who sits on the throne
and to the Lamb be praise and honor
and glory and power, for ever and
ever!"

Revelation 5:13

COPYWORK

Then I heard every creature in heaven and
on earth and under the earth and on the
sea, and all that is in them, singing:
"To him who sits on the throne and to the
Lamb be praise and honor and glory and
power, for ever and ever!"

Revelation 5:13

Pinniped Minibooks

Lesson 3

Paste your Pinnipeds Flap
Books onto this page.

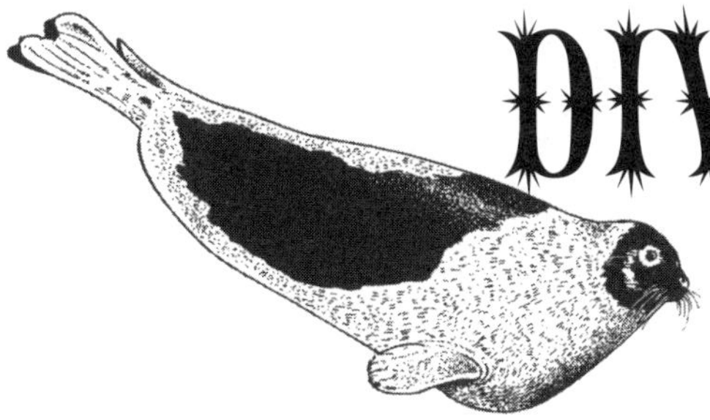

DIVE DEEPER

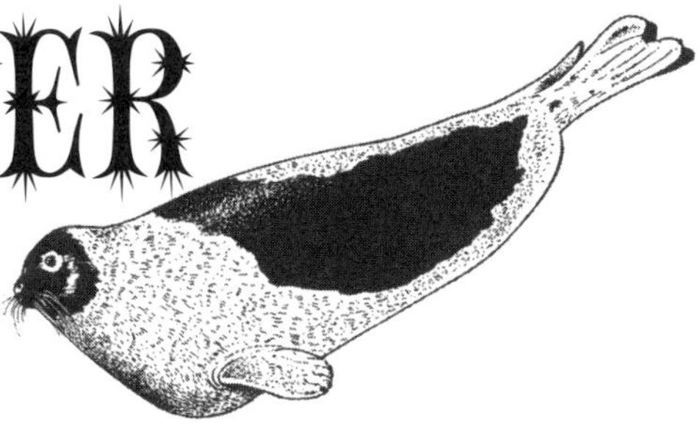

Lesson 3

Do Walruses Stay Warmer in Water or in air?

You can do an experiment to find out!

You will need:
Smooth peanut butter
A microwave
A large spoon
Tape
A bowl of room temperature water
2 cups
2 thermometers
2 popsicle sticks or wooden skewers

Heat the peanut butter in the microwave (between 80° and 90°F). Tape a popsicle stick to each thermometer so that one end of the stick extends slightly past the thermometer bulb (don't cover the bulb with tape). This will enable you to use the thermometer to stir without the bulb touching the bottom or sides of the cup or bowl. Write down the temperature of the water in the bowl. Fill the cups half-full with peanut butter. Measure the temperature of the peanut butter in each cup and write it down. Now, hold one cup of peanut butter in the pan of water (but don't touch the bottom of the pan). At the same time, hold another cup in the air. Use the two thermometers to stir the peanut butter in each cup to distribute the temperature throughout the cups. Record the temperatures every thirty seconds. What did you learn? (Go to the course website to find out what should have happened).

Create a Poster to Stop Pollution

Some Antarctic fur seals have "debris collars" on their necks made of packing bands, nylon string, and broken fishing nets. If not removed, the collars can cause open wounds and infections. They can also prevent circulation and cause strangulation as the animal grows. These things can kill the seals. Why not create a poster to help stop the pollution that causes debris collars.

Book Suggestions

Sam the Sea Cow by Francine Jacobs. This true story follows Sam from his entrapment in a sewer pipe to his ultimate release in the Crystal Rivers of Florida.
Sandy Seal: A Tale of Sea Dogs by Suzanne Tate. An interesting and factual story about the life of a young harbor seal – popularly known as a "sea dog."
Mary Manatee: A Tale of Sea Cows by Suzanne Tate. A living science book about the adventures of a sea cow named Mary. Very informative.
Andre the Famous Harbor Seal by Fran Hodgkins. A true story about a seal named Andre.
The Lost Seal by Diane McKnight. A true story about a young Weddell seal who was a long way from his natural habitat on the sea ice of McMurdo Sound. Scientists discover the seal, and he gets the ride of his life back to his natural habitat. Ages 9-12

*Be aware that some titles may contain evolutionary content

My Pinniped Project
Lesson 3

What I did:

What I learned:

Scientific Speculation Sheet

Blubber

Lesson 3

Name______________________________ Date _______________

Materials Used:

Procedure:

Hypothesis:

Results:

Conclusion:

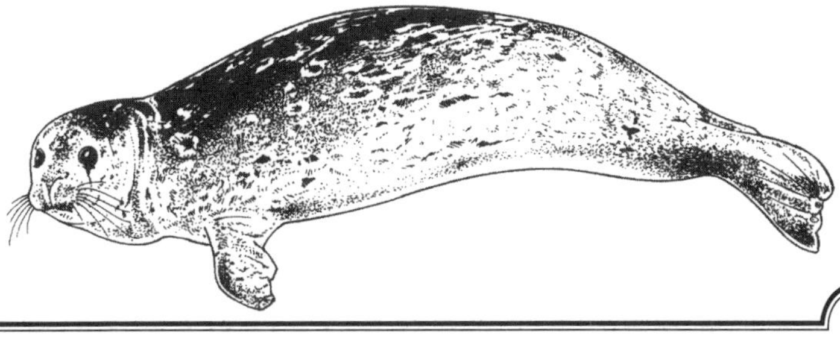

Fascinating Facts

about

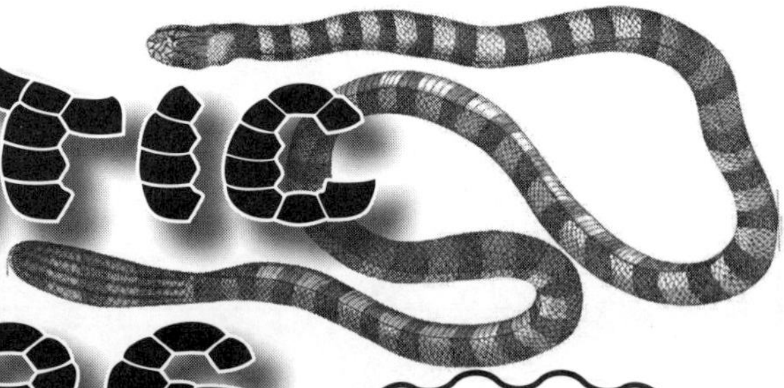

Aquatic Herps

Lesson 4

Name ____________________ Date ____________

What Do You Remember? Lesson 4 Review Questions

1. What is the name we use to mean both amphibians and reptiles?
2. Name some of the differences between mammals and reptiles.
3. How are sea turtles different from land turtles?
4. What is the top part of a turtle's shell called?
5. What term do we use to describe hibernation in herps?
6. What are some of the dangers sea turtles face?
7. What makes a sea snake different from other snakes?
8. What are the two kinds of snake venom?
9. How are reptiles different from amphibians?
10. What is the difference between most amphibians and aquatic amphibians?

Sea Turtles

Lesson 4

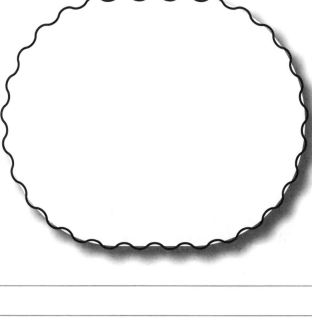

Reptile Meets Amphibian

Lesson 4

Sea Turtle Preservation

Lesson 4

COPYWORK

Just as Moses lifted up the snake in the desert, so the Son of Man must be lifted up.

John 3:14

COPYWORK

Just as Moses lifted up the snake in the desert, so the Son of Man must be lifted up.

John 3:14

VOCABULARY CROSSWORD

LESSON 4

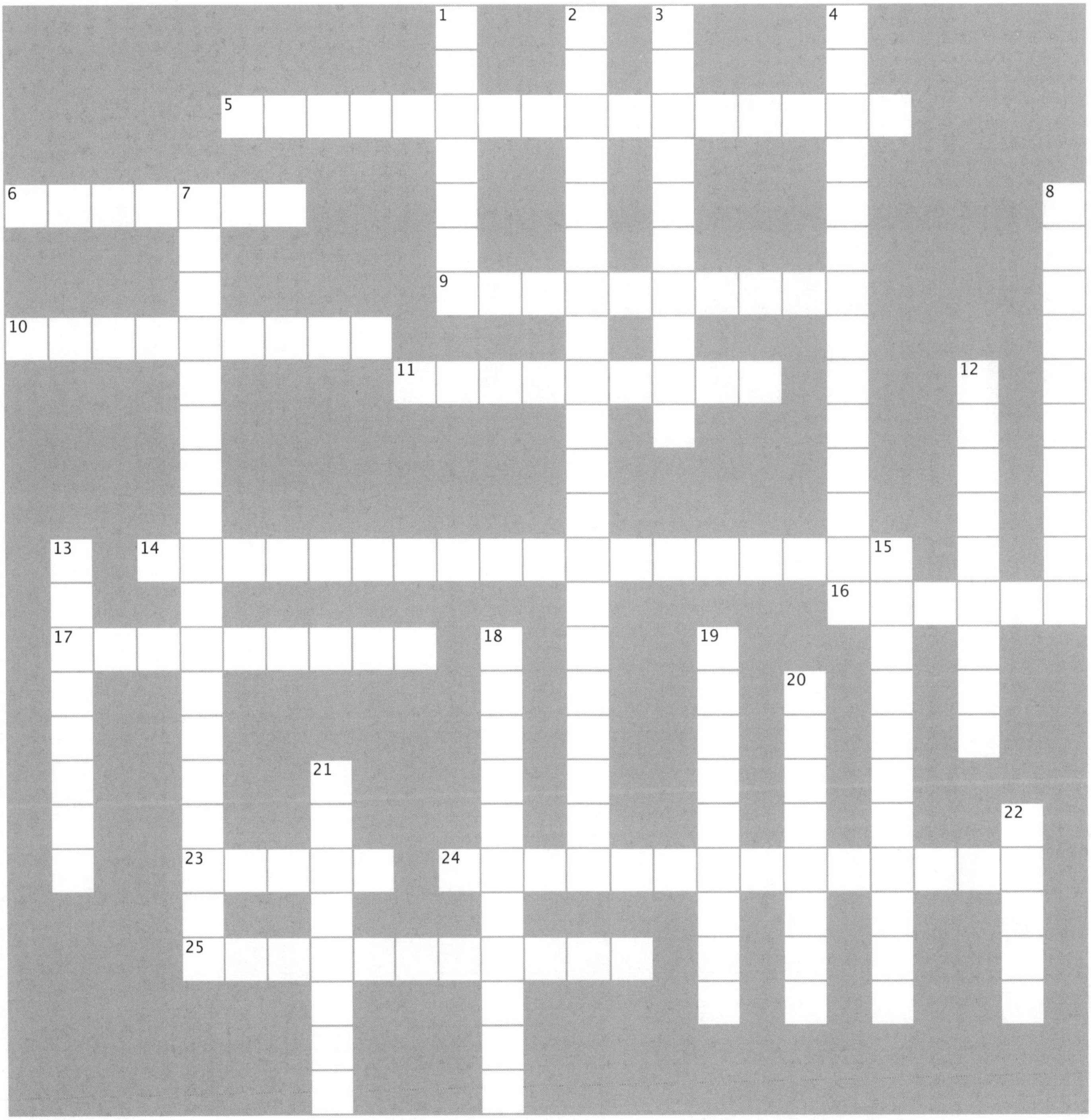

ECTOTHERMIC
TESTUDINES
PLASTRON
KERATIN
ESTIVATION
OLIVE RIDLEY
ANTIVENIN
HERPS

OVIPAROUS
CARAPACE
SCUTES
VALVED NOSTRILS
DIFFUSION
KEMP'S RIDLEY
NEUROTOXIN
CAUDATA

BRUMATION
LOGGERHEAD TURTLE
GREEN SEA TURTLE
LEATHERBACK SEA TURTLE
AUSTRALIAN FLATBACK
HAWKSBILL SEA TURTLE
MUDPUPPY
ANURA
HEMOTOXIN

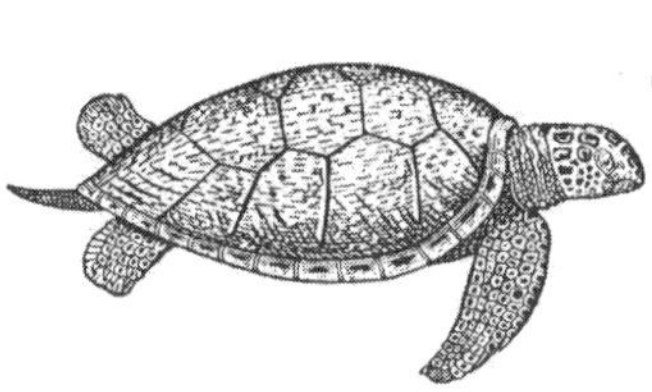

VOCABULARY CROSSWORD

Across

5. A species of sea turtle that can be spotted in the warm waters off the coast of the U.S. It is named for its large, block-like head. TWO WORDS
6. The order in which salamanders belong.
9. A type of snake venom that attacks the nervous system causing muscles (including those that help us breathe) to stop working.
10. A type of snake venom that goes into the blood system and destroys the blood's ability to travel through the body.
11. Egg-laying animals.
14. The species of sea turtle that is occasionally seen in American waters and is named for its pointed beak. THREE WORDS
16. The plates covering the carapace and the plastron.
17. A process where oxygen can get into the skin of an amphibian.
23. All frogs and toads belong to this order. Its name means "without tail."
24. A species of sea turtle that can be found on the east coast of Florida. It gets its name from the color of its body fat. THREE WORDS
25. A type of ridley sea turtle that is considered the most endangered of all sea turtles. TWO WORDS

Down

1. Scutes are made of this substance, as are fingernails.
2. The species of sea turtle that grows the largest, dives the deepest and travels the farthest of all sea turtles. THREE WORDS
3. If the weather gets too dry, amphibians go into this kind of hibernation in order to survive until it gets wet again.
4. Specially designed nostrils that can close up when a sea snake goes underwater and open when it comes up for air, much like the blowhole of a whale. TWO WORDS
7. The species of sea turtle that can only be found off the coast of Australia. TWO WORDS
8. The order in which turtles belong.
12. A state similar to hibernation, but instead of sleeping, the herp's body slows down so much that it hardly uses any energy during the winter.
13. A type of salamander that never loses its gills.
15. Cold-blooded animals are considered ___________.
18. A type of ridley sea turtle that is known for its color. It is the smallest of all sea turtles. TWO WORDS
19. A medicine that stops a snake's venom from harming the person or animal bit by a venomous snake.
20. The lower plate of the turtle's shell.
21. The upper dome of the turtle's shell.
22. Usually refers to reptiles and amphibians, and comes from the Greek word "herpeton" which means "creeping, crawling creatures that move about on their bellies."

Herps Minibooks
Lesson 4

Paste your Hatching Herps
Books onto this page.

DIVE DEEPER

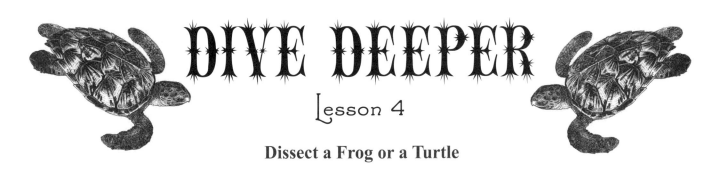

Lesson 4

Dissect a Frog or a Turtle

Although you will probably have to do this in high school biology, you can enjoy the wonders of frog and turtle dissections today! Simply purchase a frog or turtle and dissection supplies from any science supplier and print up sheets from the Internet that detail how to dissect the animals.

You can find dissection supplies at many online stores. Some of them will also sell instructions and literature related to each animal you dissect. Here are a few stores that may have supplies for this dissection:

Hometrainingtools.com – Home Training Tools
nilesbio.com – Niles Biological Supply
Carolina.com – Carolina Biological Supply
Wardsci.com – Ward's Natural Sciences

Turtle Puppet Show

Create sea turtle hand puppets with socks and felt. Write a play about your sea turtle on her journey to the place where she was born to lay her eggs. You can create puppets of other animals the turtle may encounter on her journey. Be sure to include the debris she must avoid eating (plastic bags).

Book and DVD Suggestions

Tammy Turtle: A Tale of Saving Sea Turtles by Suzanne Tate. A living science book about the adventures of a turtle named Tammy.
Turtle in the Sea by Jim Arnosky. The story of a sea turtle and what she must battle to stay alive so she can lay her eggs.
Sea Turtles by Gail Gibbons. Soft watercolor illustrations amplify brief descriptions of the eight species of sea turtles. Unique characteristics are described in a few carefully chosen words, and the pictures draw readers into the creatures' underwater world.
The Life Cycle of a Sea Turtle by Bobie Kalman. Children will learn about: the growth and development inside the turtle egg, the turtle's life as a hatchling, the dangerous journey back to the sea, and how people can help sea turtles.
One Tiny Turtle by Nicola Davies. A dramatic rendering of the life cycle of the Loggerhead turtle.
Watch Me Grow: Turtle by Lisa Magloff. Explaining each stage of development on the road to adulthood, this adorable book gives beginning readers an animal's eye view of turtles growing up.
Turtle Rescue: Changing the Future for Endangered Wildlife by Pamela Hickman. Nonfiction. This outstanding overview of the plight of the world's turtles and tortoises describes the general problems that all turtles face and explains what is being done to rescue certain species from near extinction.
The Lighthouse Family - The Turtle by Cynthia Rylant. Using only a rope and their hearts to guide them, Seabold, Lila, and Whistler make their way down the side of the cliff. And what they discover will help them weather even the thickest fog – a new friend.
Into the Sea by Brenda Z. Guiberson. Experience the life of a female sea turtle as she breaks from her shell, splashes into the sea, and navigates for survival, eventually returning to the place of her birth to lay eggs.
Turtle Bay by Saviour Pirotta. A beguiling look at the breeding process of Japanese sea turtles, who lay their eggs on land yet live in the ocean.
Turtle in the Sea by Jim Arnosky. A story about the hazards of being an adult sea turtle.
Turtle: the Incredible Journey (DVD) narrated by Miranda Richardson. This nature documentary brings marine conservation issues, such as overfishing and pollution, to the forefront of viewers' minds.

*Be aware that some titles may contain evolutionary content

My Herps Project

Lesson 4

What I did:

What I learned:

Scientific Speculation Sheet

Tadpole Growth

Lesson 4

Name______________________________ Date _______________

Materials Used:

Procedure:

Hypothesis:

Results:

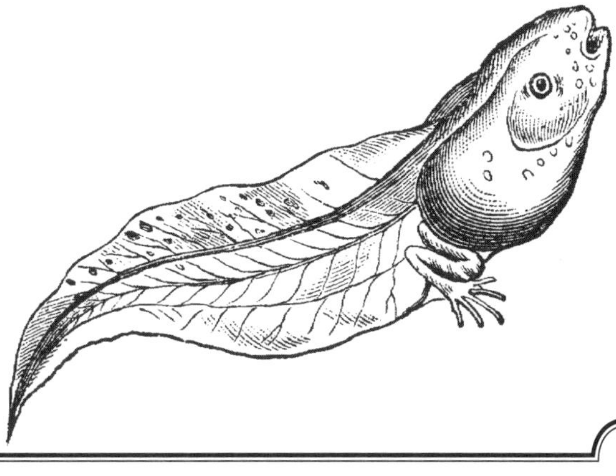

Fascinating Facts
about

LESSON 5

Name ______________________________ Date ______________

What Do You Remember? Lesson 5 Review Questions

1. Who found the first fossil of a giant "sea monster?"

2. What four kinds of large sea reptiles did we discuss?

3. Which of those four might not have spent all of its time in the sea?

4. Which two animals is a plesiosaur like, and how is it like them?

5. What did the plesiosaur eat to aid in chewing its food?

6. How do we know what an ichthyosaur looks like?

7. How is an ichthyosaur different from a fish?

8. Which of the four types of giant marine reptiles was shaped a lot like a snake and had tiny flippers?

9. What is one explanation for why we have so many sea creature fossils all over the earth?

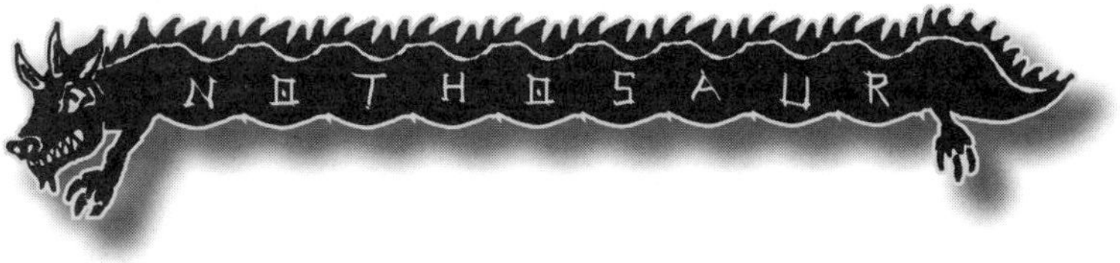
NOTHOSAUR

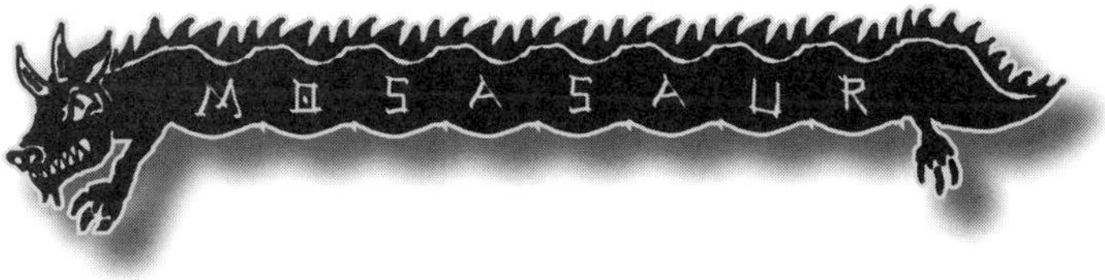
MOSASAUR

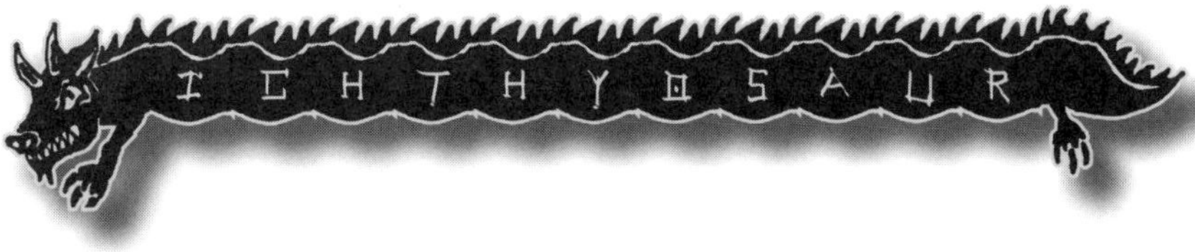
ICHTHYOSAUR

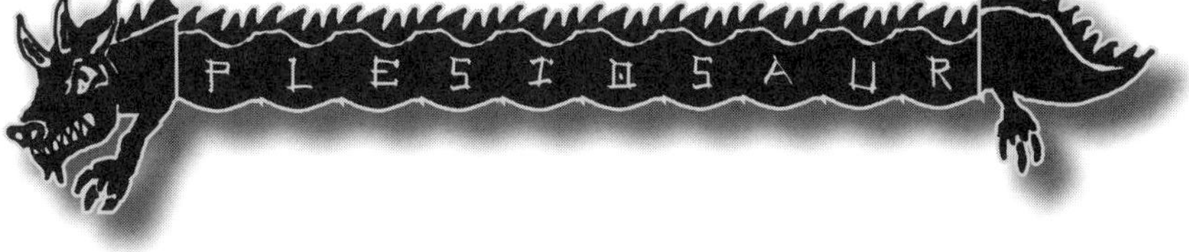
PLESIOSAUR

WHALE AND LEVIATHAN

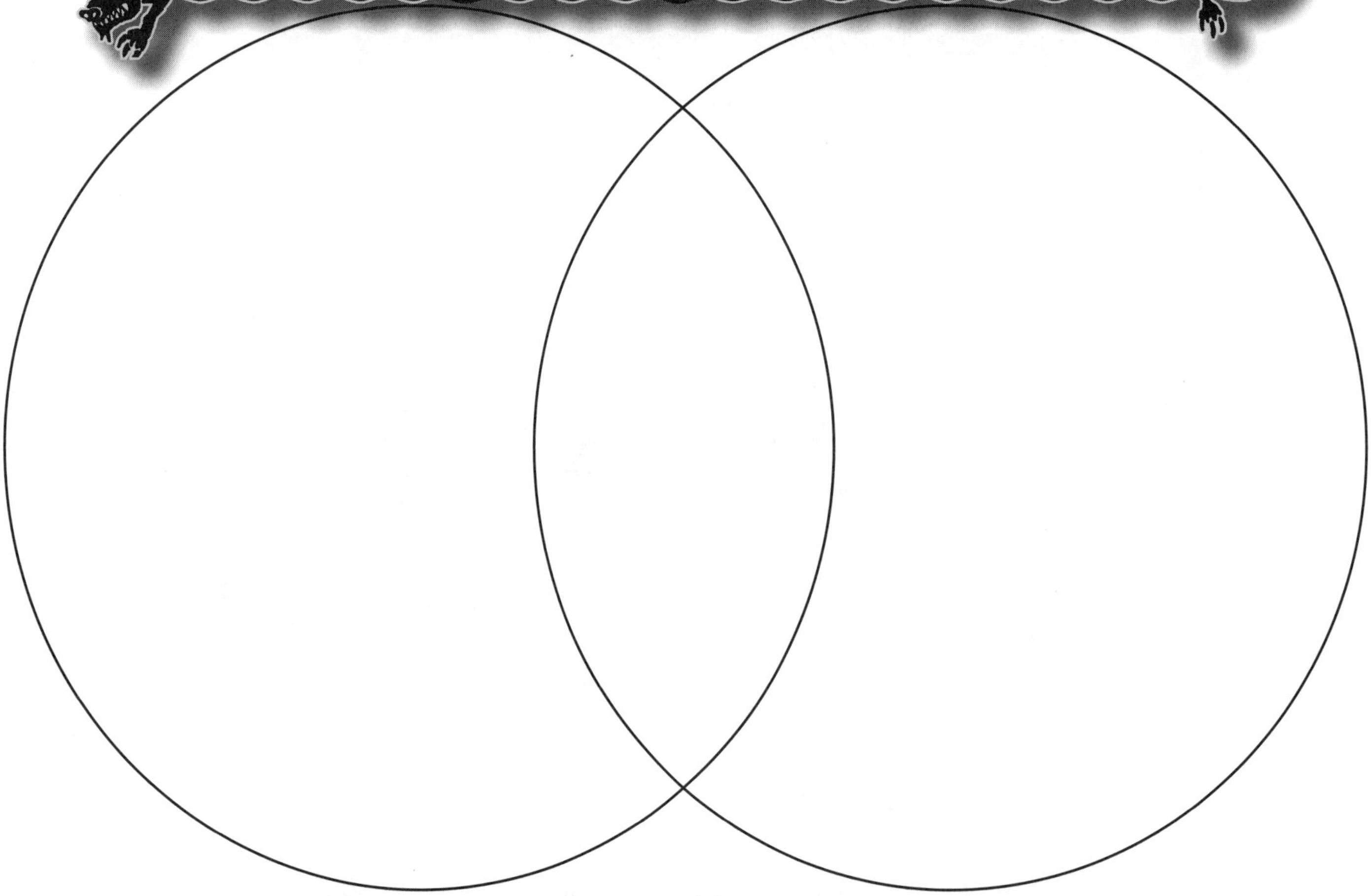

CROCODILE AND LEVIATHAN

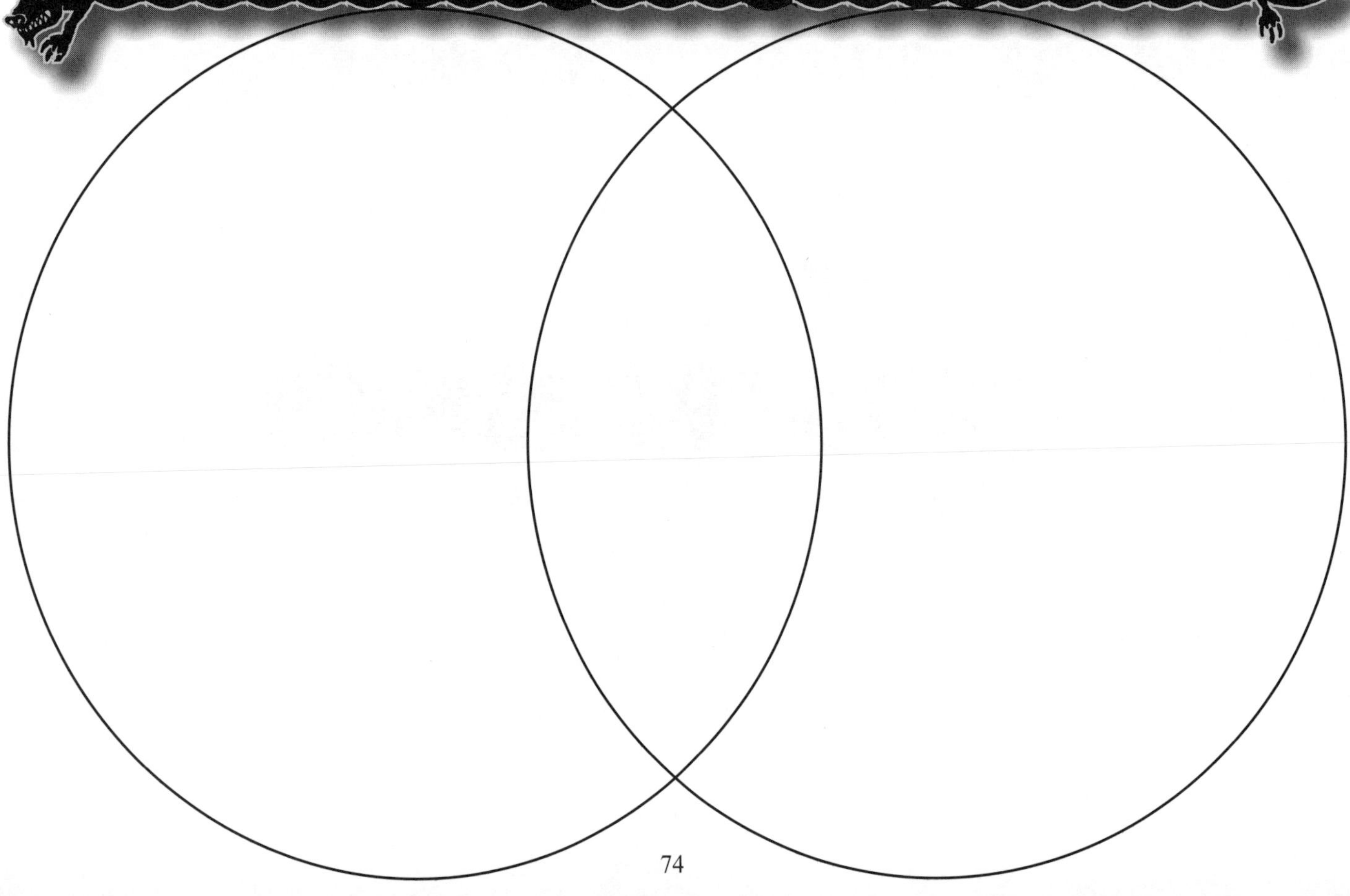

LEVIATHAN

Lesson 5

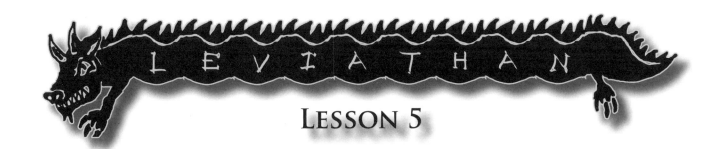

COPYWORK

Can you pull in the leviathan with a fishhook or tie down his tongue with a rope?

Job 41:1

COPYWORK

Can you pull in the leviathan
with a fishhook or tie down his
tongue with a rope?

Job 41:1

VOCABULARY CROSSWORD

LESSON 5

ICHTHYOSAURUS	PLESIOSAURUS
NOTHOSAURS	MOSASAURS
ELASMOSAURUS	PLESIOSAURIA
PLIOSAURS	GASTROLITHS
KRONOSAURUS	ARTICULATED FOSSIL

Across

1. Marine reptiles with long necks.
4. A large pliosaur measuring 30 feet long with a head that was 9 feet long.
7. The first fossilized sea creature that Mary Anning discovered on the beach.
8. What we call a fossil that is found with the bones present in their proper places, almost as if they were still all attached to each other. TWO WORDS
9. The second fossilized sea creature that Mary Anning discovered on the beach.
10. These fossilized giant marine reptiles resemble sea snakes.

Down

2. A kind of plesiosaur that looks like a snake forced into the body of a turtle.
3. Stomach stones found in the belly of a plesiosaur. They moved around in its stomach crushing the shells of the animals it ate.
5. Short-necked marine reptiles.
6. Marine mammals that looked like long-necked, long-tailed lizards with four webbed feet.

PRIMEVAL REPTILES

MINIBOOK

LESSON 5

Paste your Primeval Reptiles
Wheel onto this page.

DIVE DEEPER

Lesson 5

Book and DVD Suggestions

Dry Bones and other Fossils by Dr. Gary & Mary Parker. Look at fossil deposits, dinosaur skeletons, etc., as the Parkers discuss the topic of creation versus evolution.

Absotively, Posilutely by Carl Kerby and Dan Lietha (Illustrator). Find the absolute best evidence that God created the world! Designed for children ages 8 to 14, this entertaining and full-color book will get kids thinking logically and biblically.

Field Guide to Lake Monsters, Sea Serpents, and Other Mystery Denizens of the Deep by Loren Coleman. Filled with comprehensive drawings, classifications, and maps, this book is an invaluable resource.

The Legend of Little Nessie by Ramon Cassinari and Peter Parlagreco. An adorable 24 page storybook about the famous Loch Ness monster's baby.

Little Nessie by Julia Mowery and Marleen K. Ray. Herein lies a wonderful adventure of a boy who finds a huge egg along the bank of Loch Ness.

Nessie the Loch Ness Monster by Richard Brassey. This book contains facts (more or less true) about the Loch Ness Monster, her alleged arrival in the Loch, and what people have seen—or thought they have seen.

Giant Sea Reptiles of the Dinosaur Age by Caroline Arnold. A look at prehistoric sea creatures.

If Dinosaurs Were Alive Today by Running Press. Realistic illustrations of dinosaurs among today's animals, with details on their sizes and possible habits. Great book to incite thinking about what it would be like to have dinosaurs around today.

Sea Monsters: A Prehistoric Adventure (DVD- National Geographic) by Jerry Hoffman and Jennifer Aguilar. This 40-minute special explores the less-familiar world of the prehistoric oceans.

Chased by Dinosaurs (DVD) directed by Jasper James, Tim Haines. You'll be on the edge of your seat as zoologist Nigel Marvin goes back in time to prehistoric South America, where he witnesses the battle between history's largest predator and its even more gigantic prey. In seven different seas in seven different eras, Nigel meets scary sea scorpions, a terrifying giant squid, a massive armored fish, and the vicious sixty-foot Mosasaur!

Prehistoric Planet (DVD). The Complete Dino Dynasty From BBC Warner. The BBC's award-winning Walking With Dinosaurs is now available in an all-new, kid-friendly format: Prehistoric Planet: Dino Dynasty I! The stars of the show remain the totally life-like, utterly amazing dinosaurs themselves. A wild, truly awesome journey into the ancient past that will leave you so awe-struck, you won't even realize you're learning!

The Water Horse (DVD) directed by Jay Russell. This touching story about a boy and his friendship with a sea beast ingeniously presumes to explain the truth behind "Nessie," the Loch Ness Monster. Rated PG.

*Be aware that some titles may contain evolutionary content

MY PRIMEVAL REPTILES

PROJECT

LESSON 5

What I did:

What I learned:

Scientific Speculation Sheet

Fossil Sediment

Lesson 5

Name_______________________________ Date _______________

Materials Used:

Procedure:

Hypothesis:

Results:

Fascinating Facts about FISH

Lesson 6

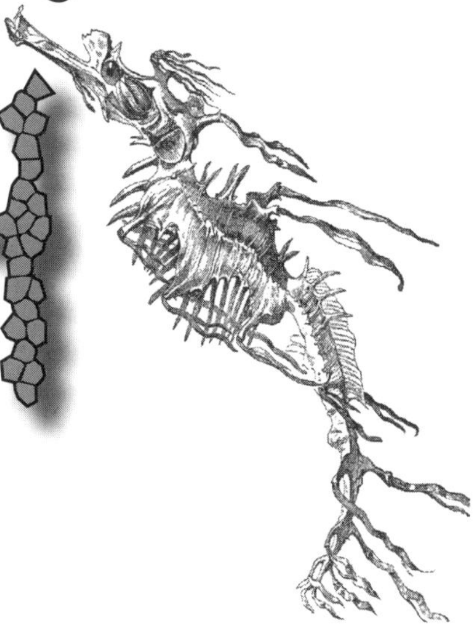

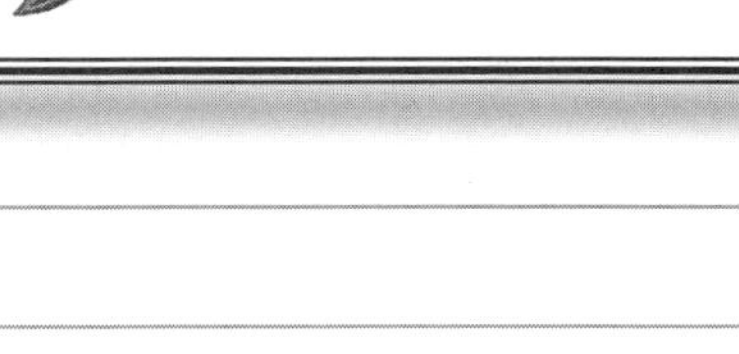

Fascinating Facts about FISH

Lesson 6

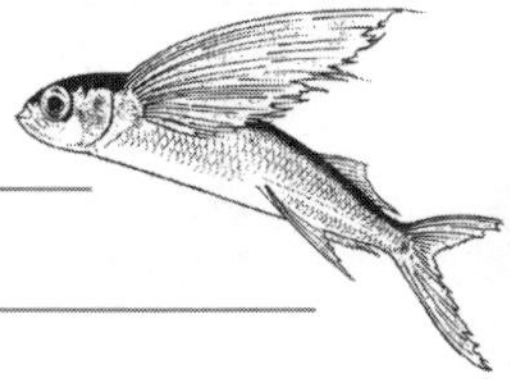

Name ______________________________ Date ____________

What Do You Remember? Lesson 6 Review Questions

1. What makes a fish a fish?

2. What fish shape is designed for fast swimming?

3. What did God give fish to help them stay buoyant in the water?

4. How many nostrils does a fish have?

5. Name two defenses that a fish might have.

6. What does "osteichthyes" mean?

7. What does a fish's lateral line do?

8. What is spawning?

9. Name a fish that makes a long journey in order to reproduce.

10. What are the five stages of a typical fish's development?

Label a Fish

Lesson 6

Pectoral Fin
Dorsal Fins
Caudal Fin
Pelvic Fin
Anal Fin

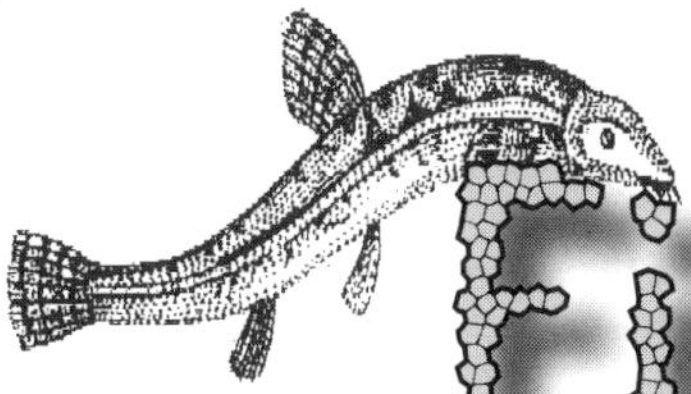

Fish Shapes

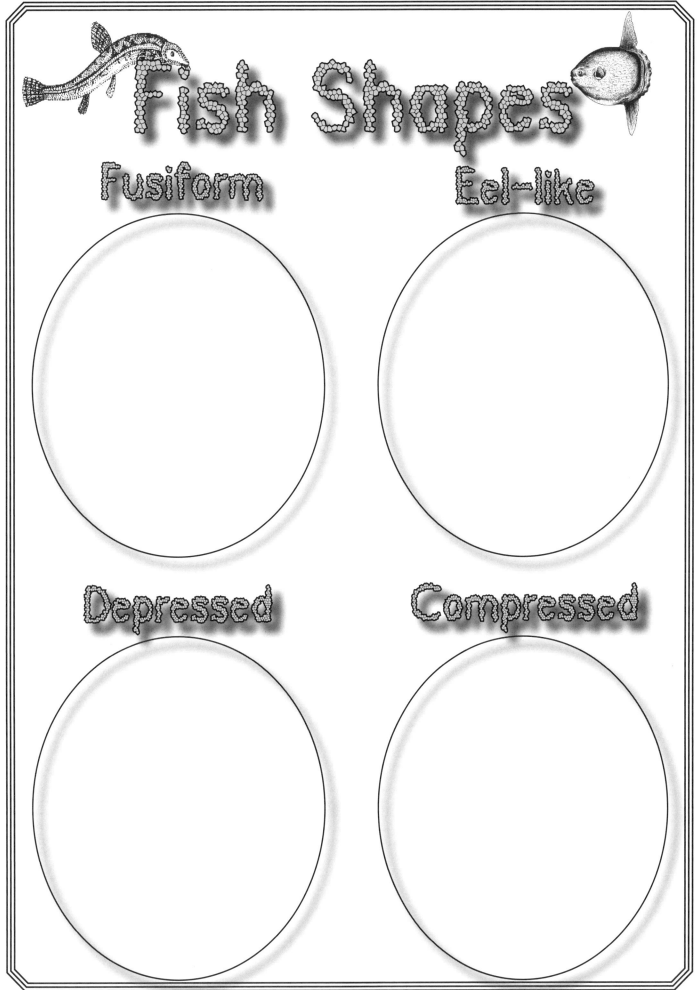

Fusiform

Eel-like

Depressed

Compressed

Fish Design

Lesson 6

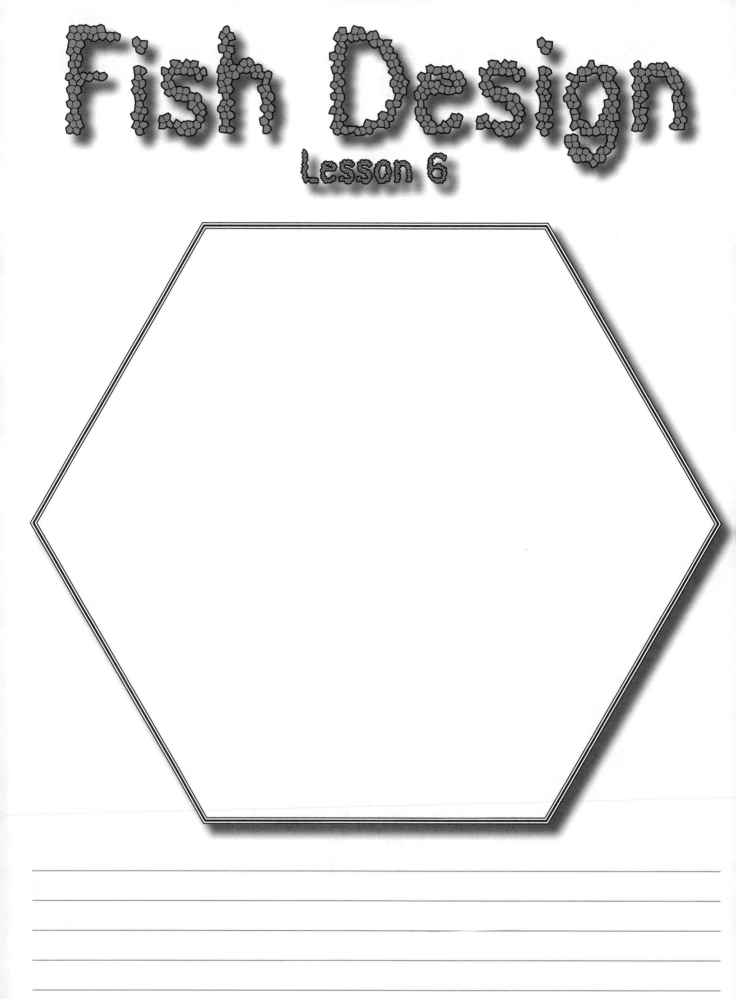

Lifecycle of a Salmon

Lesson 6

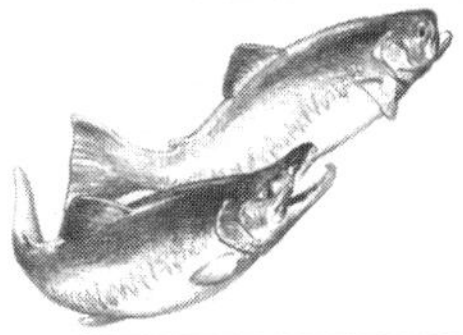

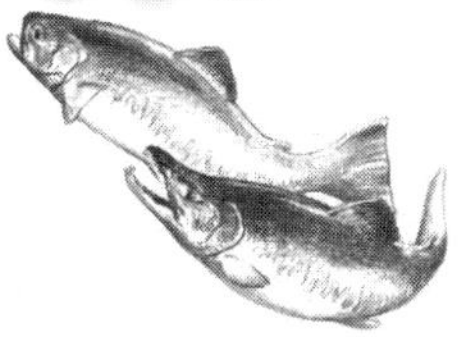

COPYWORK

"Come, follow me," Jesus said, "and I will make you fishers of men."

Mark 1:17

COPYWORK

"Come, follow me," Jesus said, "and I will make you fishers of men."

Mark 1:17

VOCABULARY CROSSWORD

LESSON 6

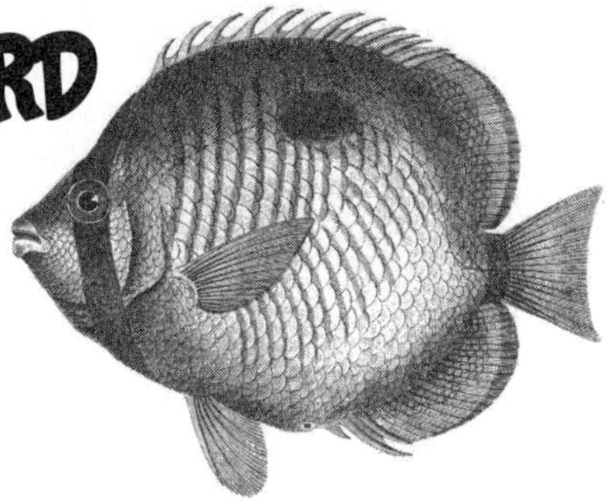

OSTEICHTHYES
PECTORAL FIN
ANAL FIN
SWIM BLADDER
MONOCULAR VISION
SPAWNING
FRY

OPERCULUM
PELVIC FIN
CAUDAL FIN
BUOYANT
LATERAL LINE
LARVAE
JUVENILE

CIRCULI
DORSAL FINS
CAMOUFLAGE
NARES
PORES
HERMAPHRODITES

Vocabulary Crossword

Lesson 6

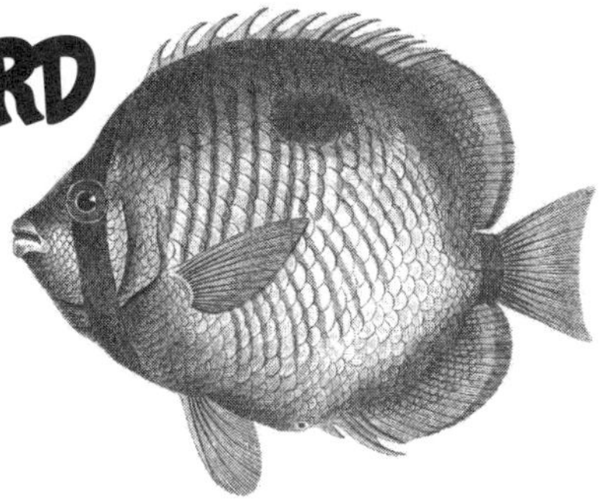

Across

6. When the male fish releases sperm on the egg. It is the most common way fishes reproduce.
7. A defense that enables an animal to disguise itself to look like the environment in which it dwells, so it is difficult for a predator to see it.
11. Fins that keep the fish from rolling side to side. They are also weapons for the fish. TWO WORDS
13. The ability to see out of each eye separately. TWO WORDS
15. Rings that are formed as the fish's scales grow.
17. A fin that keeps the fish from falling over as it swims. TWO WORDS
18. Capable of floating.
19. What we call a fish in the fourth stage of development. The fish's fins are developed, and it can swim against the current.
20. The balloon-like part in a fish's body that is filled with gas and can get larger or smaller depending on whether the fish wants to remain higher or lower in the water. TWO WORDS

Down

1. The flap over the gills of most bony fishes.
2. An extremely sensitive body feature on fishes that enables them to sense vibrations in the water. TWO WORDS
3. Narrow holes in the skin.
4. A fish's nostrils.
5. A fin on the underside of a fish that is attached to a muscle inside the fish's body and helps it move through the water. TWO WORDS
8. A fin on the side of a fish that is attached to a muscle inside the fish's body and helps it move through the water. TWO WORDS
9. Animals that have both male and female characteristics, usually changing from a male into female.
10. The fish's tail. TWO WORDS
12. The class to which fishes with bones belong.
14. What we call free-swimming larvae from the time they hatch to their juvenile stages.
16. What a fish hatches into from an egg (plural).

FISHES MINIBOOK

Lesson 6

Paste your Fish Bowl Pull Up
onto this page.

DIVE DEEPER

Lesson 6

Dissect a Fish

You can learn more about the design of a fish by dissecting one. Obtain a fish from a science supplier and enjoy learning all about them up close!

You can find dissection supplies at many online stores. Some of them will also sell instructions and literature related to each animal you dissect. Here are a few stores that may have supplies for this dissection:

Hometrainingtools.com – Home Training Tools
nilesbio.com – Niles Biological Supply
Carolina.com – Carolina Biological Supply
Wardsci.com – Ward's Natural Sciences

Print a Fish (You Can Gyotaku, Too!)

Get a whole fish from your local grocery store. Wash the fish with soap and water. Carefully dry the fish making sure not to rub off the scales. Clip off any sharp spines with pliers. Place the fish on several layers of newspaper. Plug the fish's anus (the opening just in front of the anal fin) with a small wad of paper towels. Apply a thin coat of paint to the fish. Place a T-shirt carefully over the fish. With your fingers, press it firmly over the fish, head to tail. Do not wrinkle the fabric or move it around too much once you have set it in place. Carefully remove the T-shirt from head to tail. You can make a second print immediately after without adding more paint. Rcpeat this procedure to make more Gyotaku T's. You can use paint to add embellishments to your fish.

Book and Game Suggestions

Stevie B. Sea Horse: A Tale of a Proud Papa by Suzanne Tate. Delightful explanation of the life of a sea horse.
Lucky Lookdown: A Tale of Funny Fish by Suzanne Tate. Charming tale of a little lookdown fish living at a science center.
Old Reddy Drum: A Tale of Redfish by Suzanne Tate. Old Reddy Drum, a wise and powerful fish, gives life-saving advice to young Peter Puppy Drum.
Ellie and Ollie Eel: A Tale of a Fantastic Voyage by Suzanne Tate. Delightfully explains the incredible life cycle of eels.
A Fish Out of Water by Helen Palmer. A fish rapidly outgrows its bowl, a vase, a cook pot, a bathtub...what will happen next?
Go Fish! Hawaii (card game) by Elanie de Man. A popular game containing die-cut magnets depicting actual fish you might see while swimming, snorkeling, or diving in Hawaii.

*Be aware that some titles may contain evolutionary content

MY FISH PROJECT

Lesson 6

What I did:

What I learned:

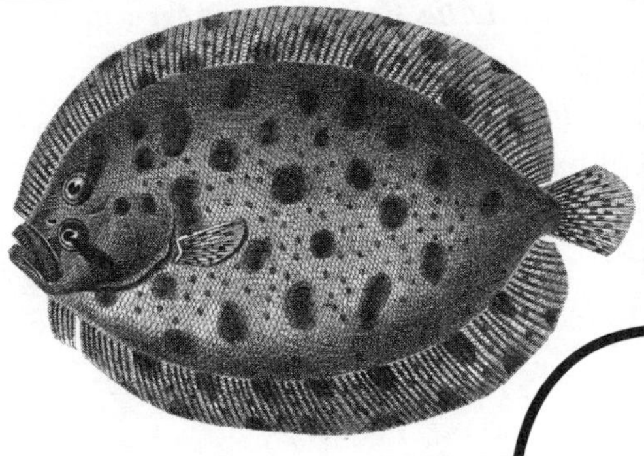

Scientific Speculation Sheet

Fish Temperature

Lesson 6

Name________________________ Date ____________

Materials Used:

Procedure:

Hypothesis:

Results:

Fascinating Facts

about

SHARKS AND RAYS

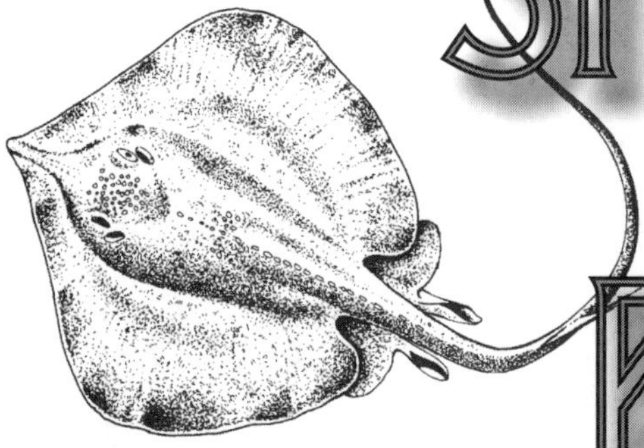

LESSON 7

Fascinating Facts about SHARKS AND RAYS

LESSON 7

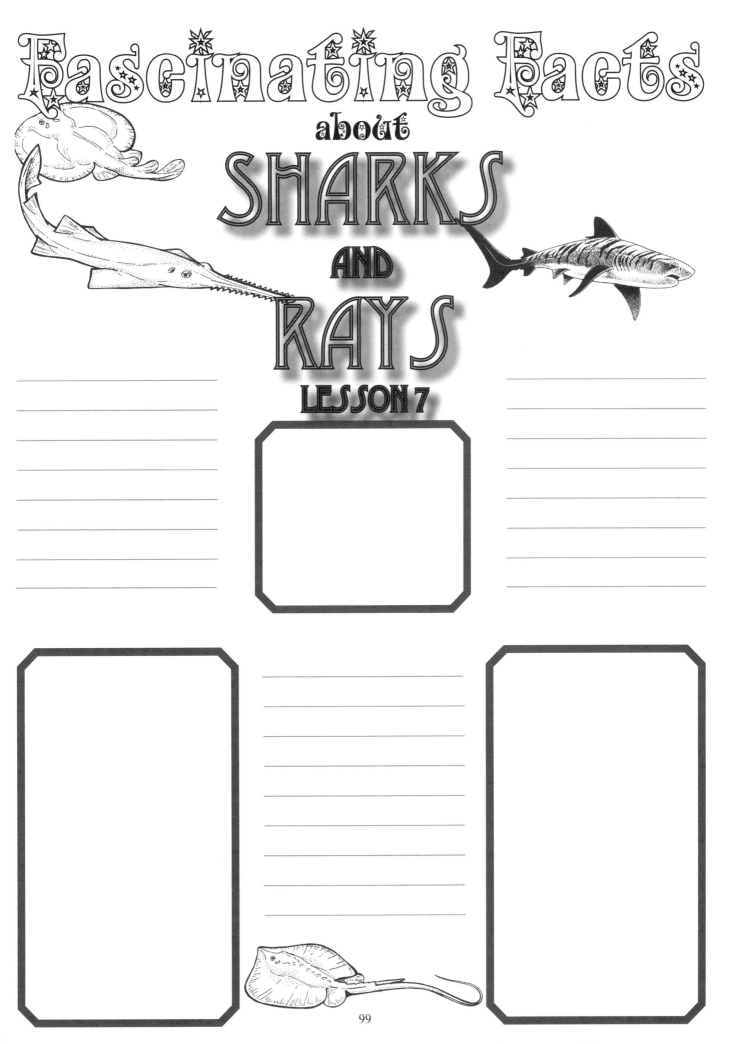

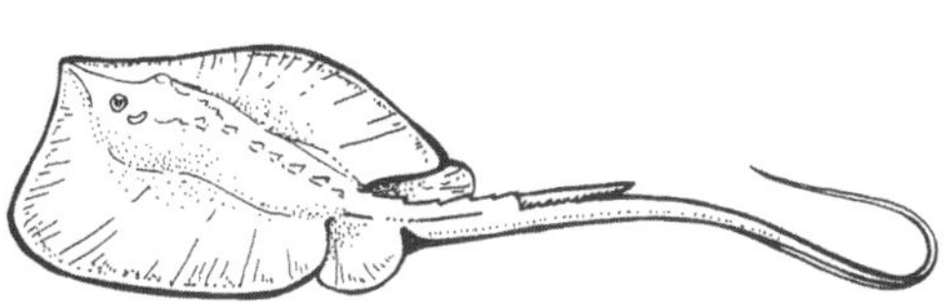

Name ____________________ Date ____________________

What Do You Remember? Lesson 7 Review Questions

1. What does the word "chondrichthyes" mean?

2. What are the scales of sharks and rays like?

3. How are the fins of bony fish and sharks different?

4. Why do sharks and rays sink when they are not swimming?

5. What is the difference between a manta ray and a stingray?

6. How can you tell the size of a shark by its teeth?

7. How do the ampullae of Lorenzini help a shark?

8. If you are swimming in the ocean and see a shark, what should you do?

9. What does "Agnatha" mean?

10. What does "anadromous" mean?

11. What are some differences between the way a hagfish feeds and the way a lamprey feeds?

12. What do almost all fishes have that the hagfish doesn't have?

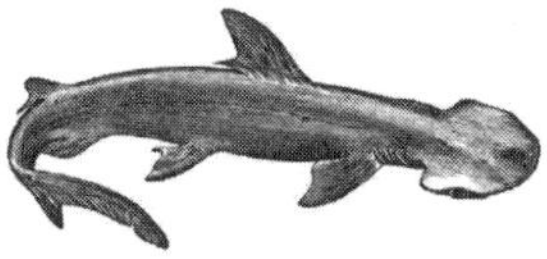

SHARKS

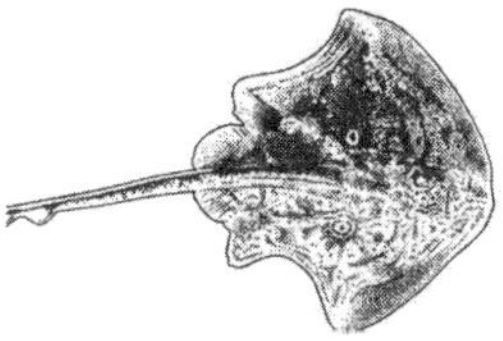

RAYS

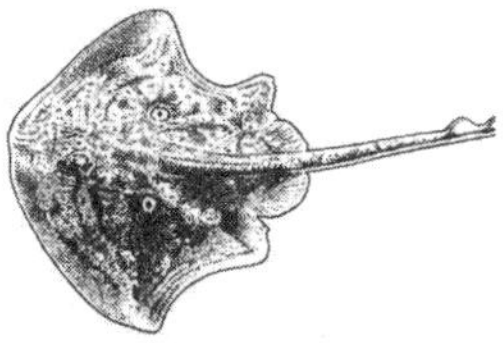

LAMPREY

HAGFISH

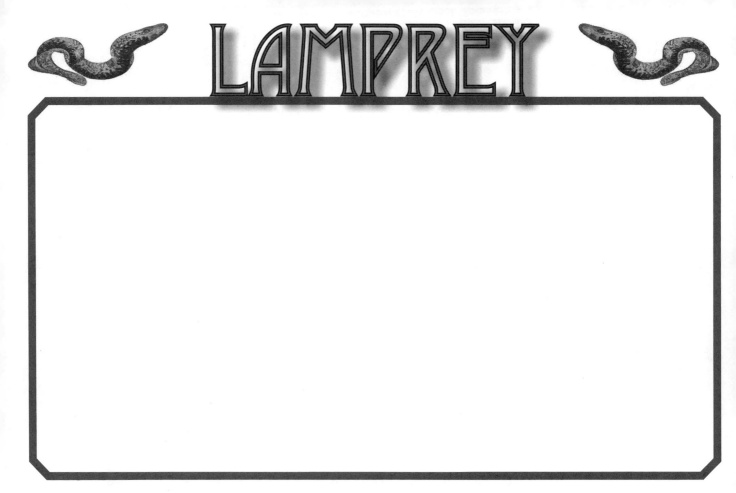

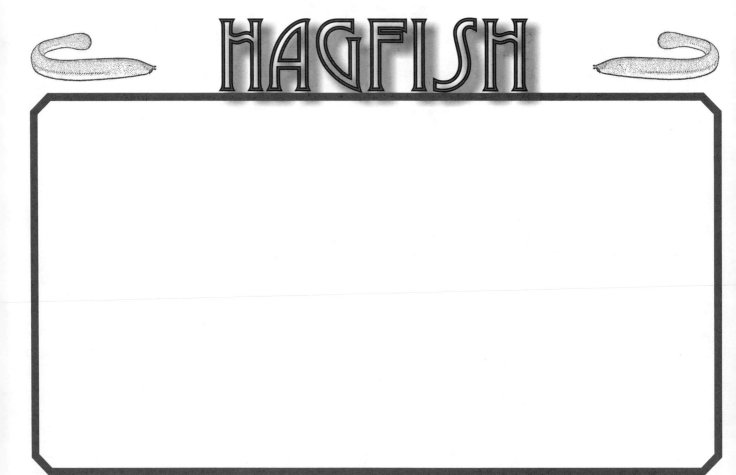

SHARK BITES

LESSON 7

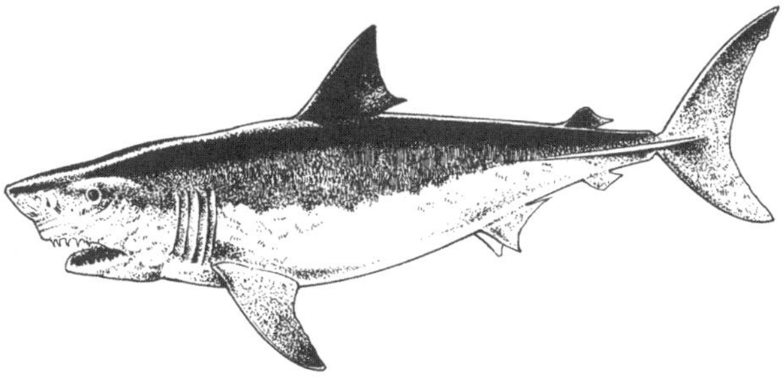

COPYWORK

So God created the great creatures of the sea and every living and moving thing with which the water teems, according to their kinds... And God saw that it was good.

Genesis 1:21

COPYWORK

So God created the great creatures of the sea and every living and moving thing with which the water teems, according to their kinds... And God saw that it was good.

Genesis 1:21

VOCABULARY CROSSWORD

LESSON 7

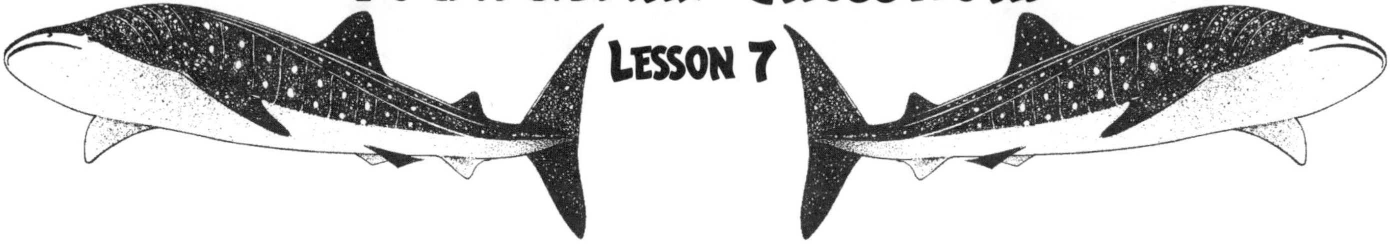

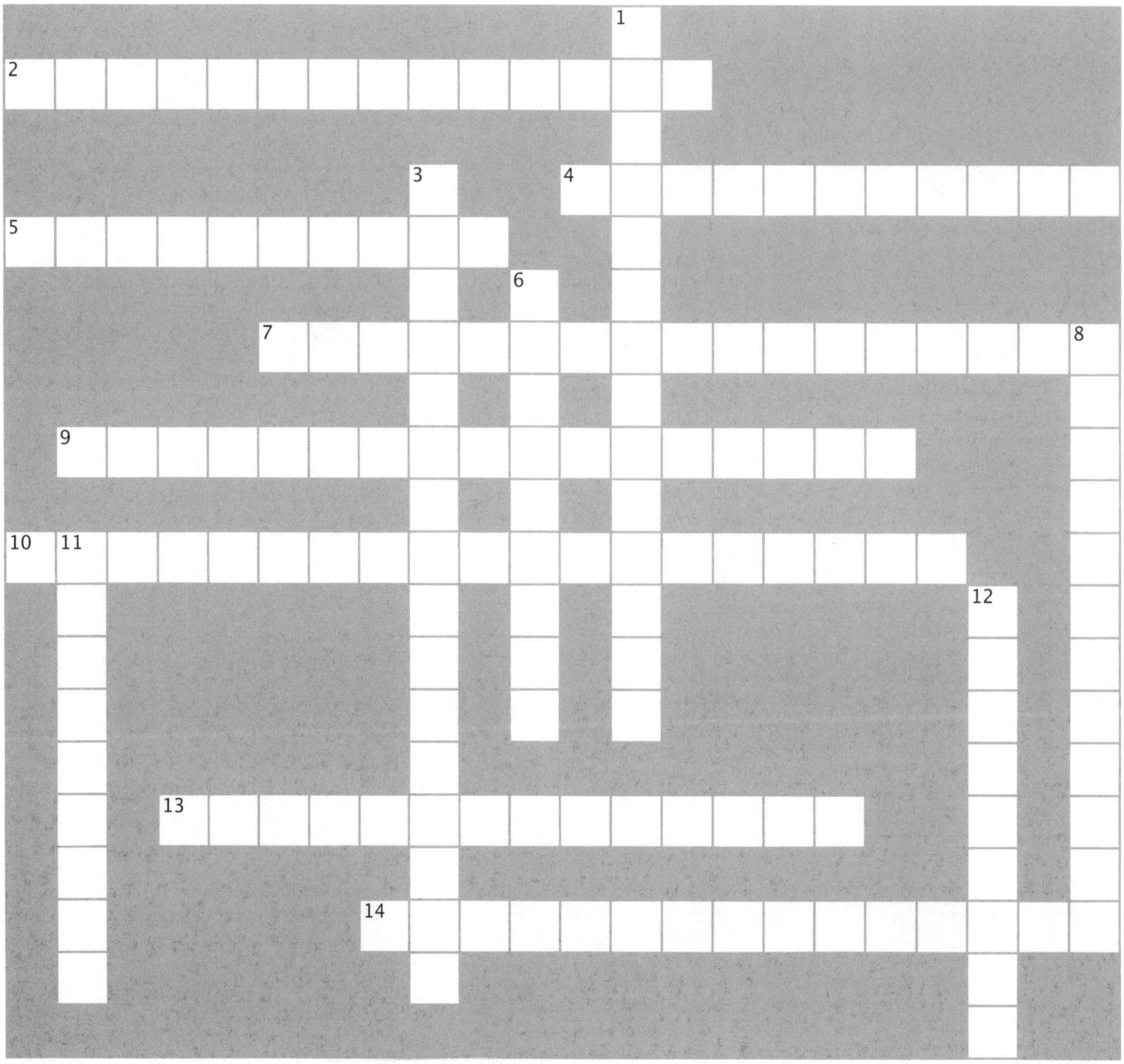

CARTILAGE	**CHONDRICHTHYES**	**DERMAL DENTICLES**
SPIRACLES	**MEGALODON**	**CARCHARHINIFORMES**
LAMNIFORMES	**SQUALIFORMES**	**ORECTOLOBIFORMES**
SQUATINIFORMES	**HEXANCHIFORMES**	**AMPULLAE OF LORENZINI**
GILL RAKERS	**HETERODONTIFORMES**	

VOCABULARY CROSSWORD

LESSON 7

Across

2. The order to which angelsharks and monkfish belong.
4. The order in which the great white shark belongs, and other sharks that grow fairly large.
5. The bristly structures on a whale shark's gills that catch plankton floating in the water. TWO WORDS
7. Sharks in this order are called ground sharks, because they tend to wander around close to the sea floor.
9. This order contains the bullhead sharks and hornsharks.
10. The nerve receptors in a shark that sense electricity in the water. THREE WORDS
13. Fishes that have skeletons made out of cartilage instead of bone.
14. Cartilaginous fish have these kind of scales. They are more like tiny teeth. TWO WORDS

Down

1. This order contains the sharks that have "extra" gill slits.
3. This order contains sharks that have their mouths on the fronts of their heads, like the whale shark and nurse shark.
6. The flexible, rubbery substance that shapes the inside of the nose and ears and forms the bones of some fish.
8. The order that contains deep-water sharks that are rounded in the middle and have short snouts.
11. An enormous shark that, as far as we know, is now extinct.
12. Breathing holes on top of a ray's body.

SHARKS & RAYS MINIBOOKS

LESSON 7

Paste your Sharks and Rays
Pop Up Books onto this page.

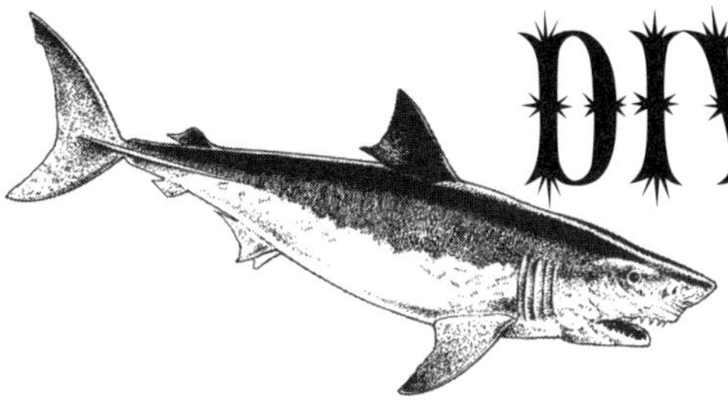

DIVE DEEPER

Lesson 7

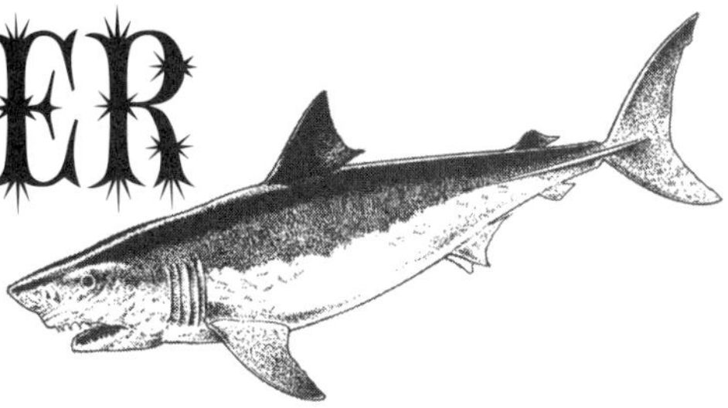

Make Hagfish Slime

You will need:
An adult – as this involves extremely hot liquid
1 tsp Metamucil or similar soluble fiber
1 cup water
A microwave safe bowl
A microwave oven
Food coloring (optional)

Mix 1 tsp of Metamucil with 1 cup (8 ounces) of water in a microwave safe bowl. You can add a drop or two of food coloring if you wish. Microwave the mixture on high for 4-5 minutes until it is bubbling. Let the mixture cool slightly, then microwave it again. The more you microwave it, the more rubbery the substance will become. After 5-6 times, CAREFULLY pour the "slime" onto a cookie sheet. Allow it to cool. It should be clammy, but not sticky. If the slime is sticky then the amount of water used needs to be reduced. Once it is cool, you can play with your hagfish slime. It can be stored at room temperature in a sealed bag for several months. It will last a very long time if you keep your slime in a sealed bag in the refrigerator.

Dissect a Lamprey or a Shark

Would you like to see the innards of a shark or lamprey (or even a hagfish)? You can by dissecting one! Simply purchase a shark or lamprey and dissection supplies from any science supplier and print up sheets from the Internet that detail how to dissect the animals. Try nilesbio.com to obtain a lamprey or hagfish.

Create a Card Game

Patterning it after Old Maid, create a card game using lots of different fish, designating the Great White Shark as the Old Maid.

Book Suggestions

Rosie Ray: A Tale of Watery Wings by Suzanne Tate. Discover many facts about the spotted eagle ray, an elegant creature that leaps from the water and soars like an eagle.
Great Sharky Shark: A Tale of a Big Hunter by Suzanne Tate. A living book detailing fascinating shark facts with lessons about the impact humans have on sea life and the environment.
The Shark Dictionary by Sarah Gustafson. Brief alphabetical entries identify different kinds of sharks and various aspects of their bodies and behavior.
A Sea Full of Sharks by Betsy Maestro. Brightly illustrated with full-color drawings on almost every page, this overview provides enough specific details on sharks to be a useful addition to any collection.
The Great White Man-Eating Shark: A Cautionary Tale by Margaret Mahy. This funny tale written by best-selling author, Margaret Mahy, will amuse and delight children everywhere.

*Be aware that some titles may contain evolutionary content

MY PROJECT

LESSON 7

What I did:

What I learned:

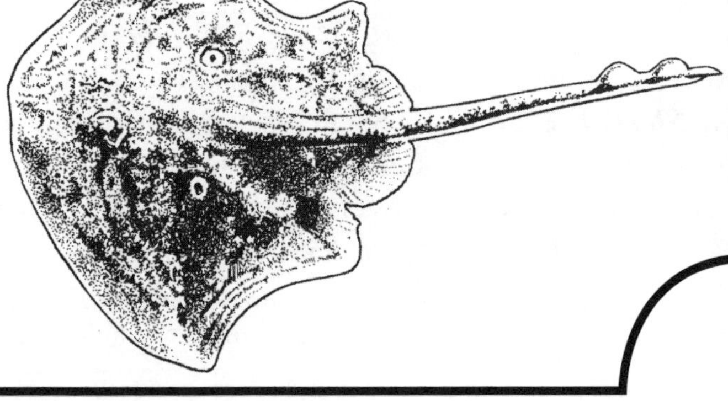

Scientific Speculation Sheet

Electricity in Salt Water

Lesson 7

Name___________________________ Date ______________

Materials Used:

Procedure:

Hypothesis:

Results:

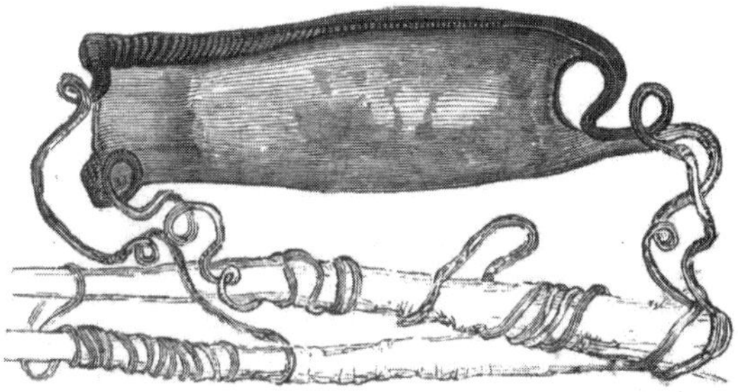

Fascinating Facts about CRUSTACEANS

LESSON 8

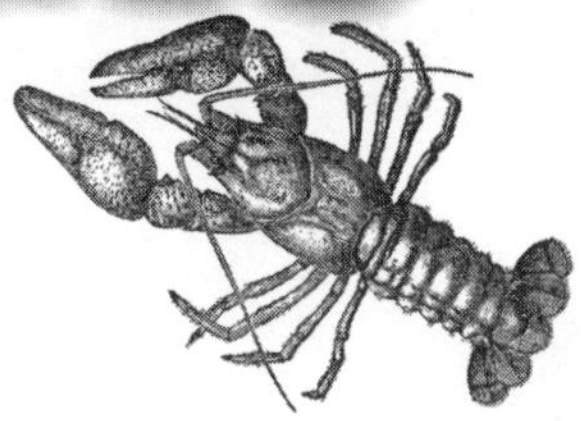

Fascinating Facts
about
Crustaceans
Lesson 8

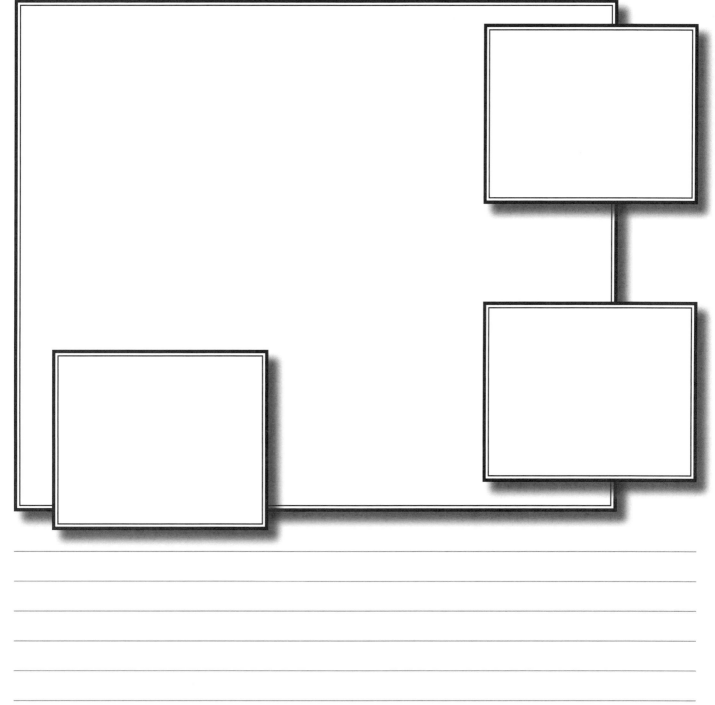

Fascinating Facts

about

CRUSTACEANS

LESSON 8

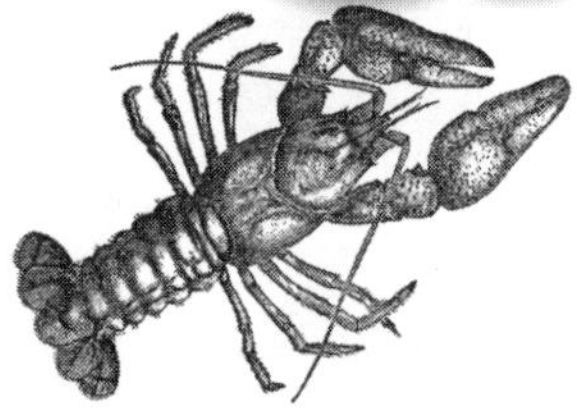

Name ______________________________ Date ______________

What Do You Remember?
Lesson 8 Review Questions

1. What does the word "arthropod" mean?

2. What is an exoskeleton?

3. How does a crustacean molt?

4. How do antennae help crustaceans?

5. What are maxillipeds?

6. What are chelipeds?

7. What are some of the uses of swimmerets?

8. How long can a lobster live?

9. How are crabs different from lobsters?

10. What is the symbiotic relationship between shrimp and fish?

11. What does it mean to be a keystone species?

12. Which crustacean is a keystone species?

13. Where do barnacles live?

14. Where do horseshoe crabs lay their eggs?

15. What kind of eyes did trilobites have?

CRUSTACEAN

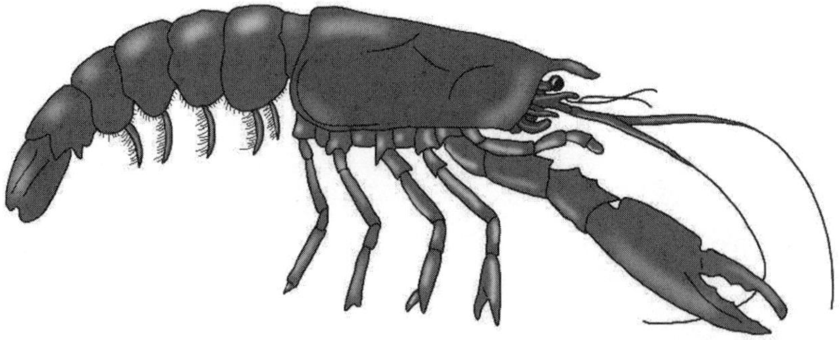

Abdomen
Swimmerets
Tail Fan
Cephalothorax
Walking Legs

Compound Eye
Antennules
Carapace
Cheliped
Antennae

CRAB

Horseshoe Crab Meets a Crab

Lesson 8

COPYWORK

For in six days the LORD made
the heavens and the earth, the
sea, and all that is in them, but he
rested on the seventh day.

Exodus 20:11

COPYWORK

For in six days the LORD made the heavens and the earth, the sea, and all that is in them, but he rested on the seventh day.

Exodus 20:11

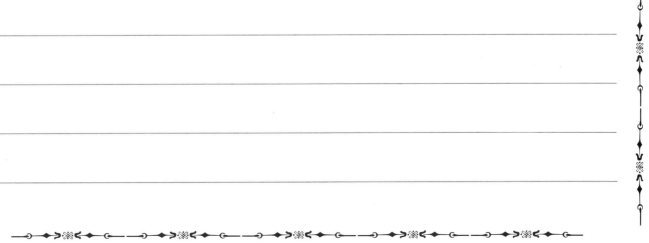

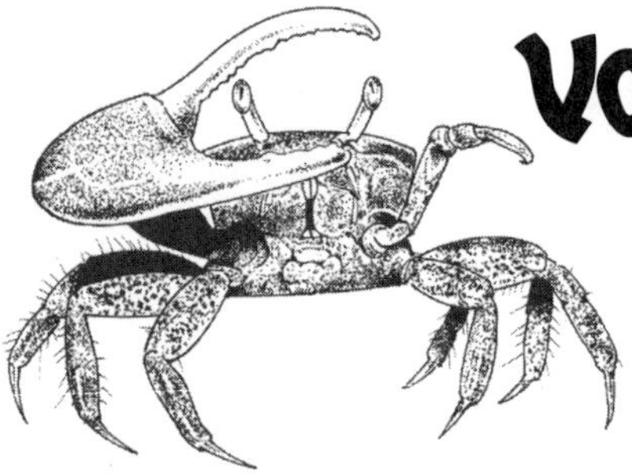

VOCABULARY CROSSWORD

LESSON 8

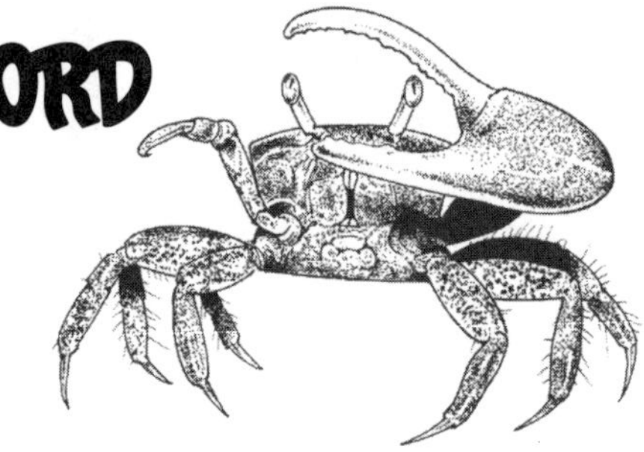

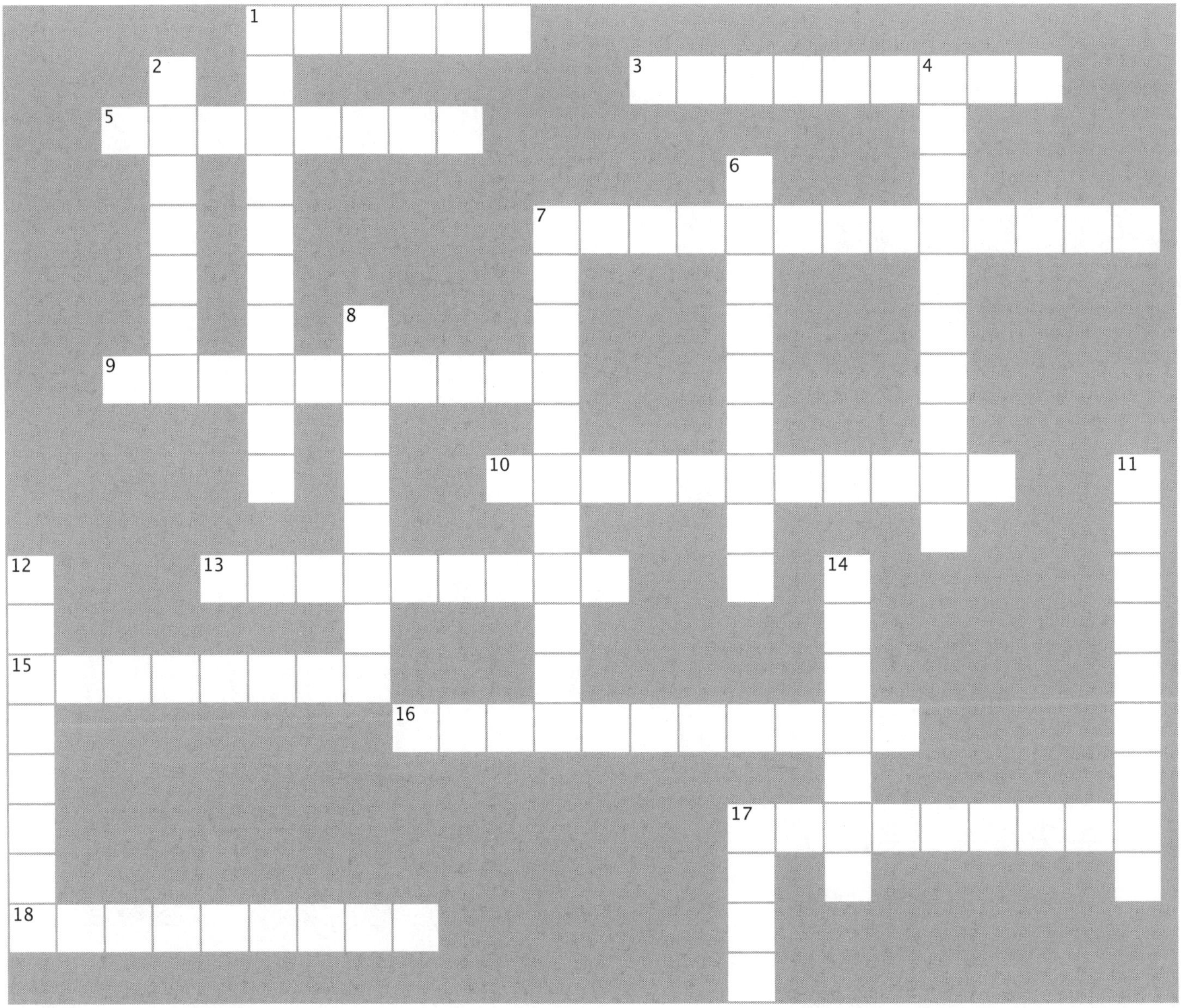

CRUSTACEANS
ABDOMEN
ANTENNAE
MAXILLAE
SYMBIOSIS
CEPHALOTHORAX
CHELIPEDS
SHRIMP
ARTHROPODS
CARAPACE
TAIL FAN
MUTUALISM
ANTENNULES
DECAPODS
CRAB
EXOSKELETON
MANDIBLES
CANNIBALS
BARNACLES
MAXILLIPEDS
SWIMMERETS

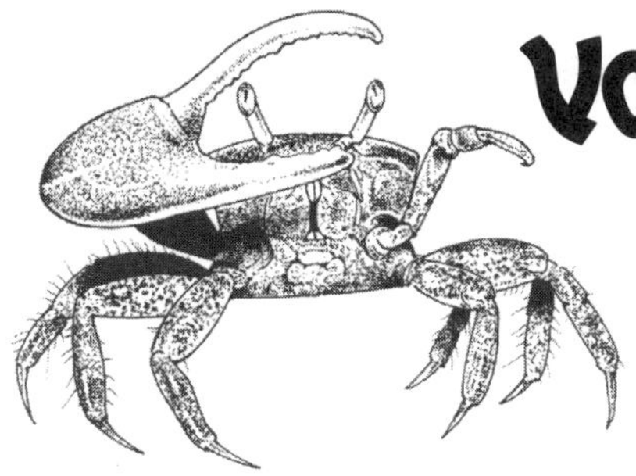

Vocabulary Crossword

Lesson 8

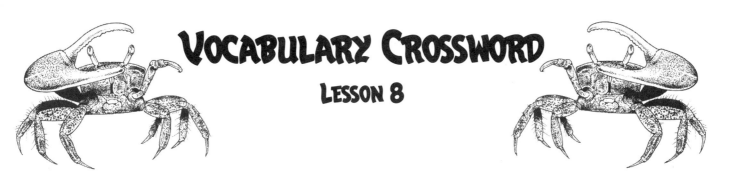

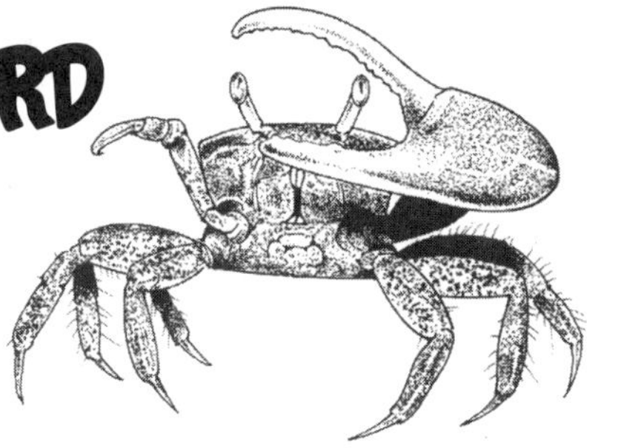

Across

1. A type of crustacean that looks like a miniature lobster.
3. Creatures that eat their own kind or species.
5. The part of the crustacean's mouth that tears the food into smaller pieces.
7. The middle part of a crustacean's body.
9. These small antennae help the crustacean keep its balance and allow it to touch and taste things.
10. The part of a crustacean's mouth that is used to hold, touch and even taste the food.
13. True crustaceans which permanently attach themselves to a hard substrate.
15. The part of the exoskeleton that covers the cephalothorax.
16. A skeleton on the outside of the animal's body.
17. The crustacean's claw-feet that are used to fight and capture prey.
18. When two or more different creatures live together in a close relationship.

Down

1. The small leg-looking paddles under the crustacean's abdomen that help propel the crustacean through the water.
2. Located at the end of the abdomen, crustaceans use this for steering while they swim. TWO WORDS
4. Creatures that have exoskeletons as well as jointed feet and legs.
6. The part of a crustacean's mouth that chews the food.
7. Marine insects with a shell.
8. Long structures on a crustacean's head that are sensitive, giving the crustacean strong senses of touch and taste.
11. When the creatures in a symbiotic relationship help each other.
12. Crustaceans that have ten legs.
14. The fleshy "tail" portion of arthropods.
17. A type of crustacean that is considered a decapod, having ten legs.

CRUSTACEANS MINIBOOKS

LESSON 8

Paste your Crustacean Accordion Books onto this page.

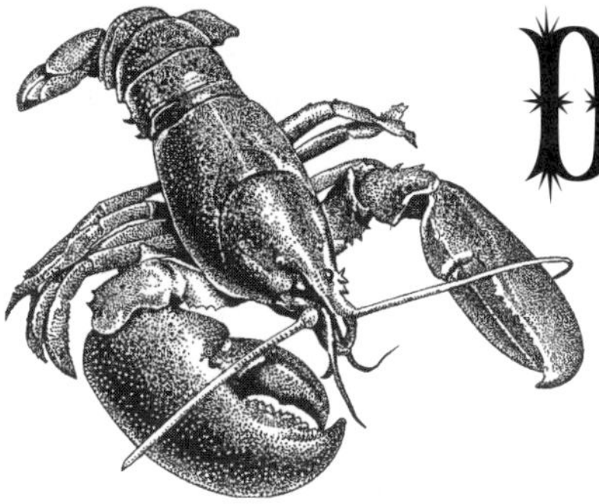

DIVE DEEPER

Lesson 8

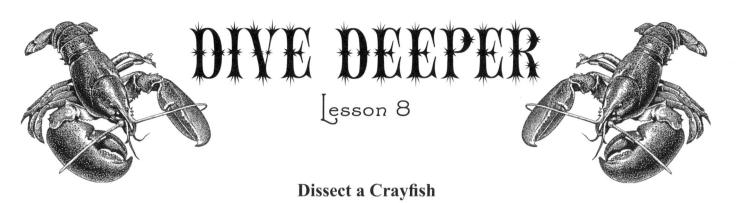

Dissect a Crayfish

There are many science suppliers that sell crayfish for dissection. If instructions are not included, you can print some with worksheets off the Internet. Simply do a search for "crayfish dissection." See if you can identify all the crayfish parts from the book!

You can find dissection supplies at many online stores. Some of them will also sell instructions and literature related to each animal you dissect. Here are a few stores that may have supplies for this dissection:

Hometrainingtools.com – Home Training Tools
nilesbio.com – Niles Biological Supply
Carolina.com – Carolina Biological Supply
Wardsci.com – Ward's Natural Sciences

My Favorite Crustacean

Do some research to discover all the different kinds of crustaceans found in the ocean. Choose your favorite one and gather as much information about that particular crustacean as you can. Be sure to study its scientific name, finding out what it means in English. Why was it given that name? After gathering your information, create a special fact page about your crustacean. Enhance your page with colorful illustrations. You can create a book with your siblings or friends by putting everyone's crustacean fact pages together.

Book Suggestions

Crab Moon by Ruth Horowitz. One night Daniel finds the beach covered with horseshoe crabs. The next morning, one lone crab is stranded. Can Daniel help?
Lindie Lobster, A Tale of Big Clawsby by Suzanne Tate. Very informative living book on the life of a single lobster named Lindie.
Crabby and Nabby: A Tale of Two Blue Crabs by Suzanne Tate. Informative living science book about two crabs and their adventures.
Happy Hermit Crab, A Tale of Shell Seekers by Suzanne Tate. A living book with interesting natural history facts about hermit crabs and why they must seek the safety of shells.
Harry Horseshoe Crab, A Tale of Crawly Creatures by Suzanne Tate. A living book with interesting facts about horseshoe crabs and how they save human lives every day.
Flossie Flounder: A Tale of Flat Fish by Suzanne Tate. A tale developed around the interesting fact that a baby flounder looks different from its parents.
A House for Hermit Crab by Eric Carle. Kids will love this rich, affectionate portrayal of Hermit Crab's ocean odyssey, and the gentle story may help them see that giving up the old for the new is not a loss, but an opportunity. (Ages 4 to 8)

*Be aware that some titles may contain evolutionary content

MY CRUSTACEAN PROJECT
LESSON 8

What I did:

What I learned:

Fascinating Facts about MOLLUSKS

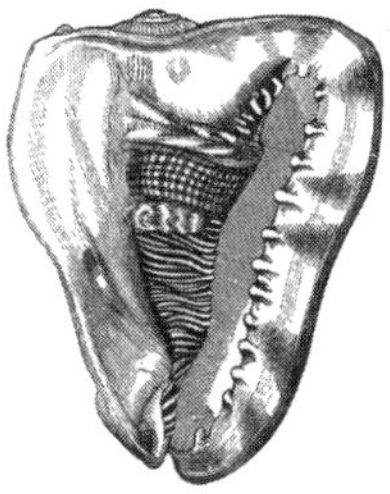

Lesson 9

Fascinating Facts about MOLLUSKS

Lesson 9

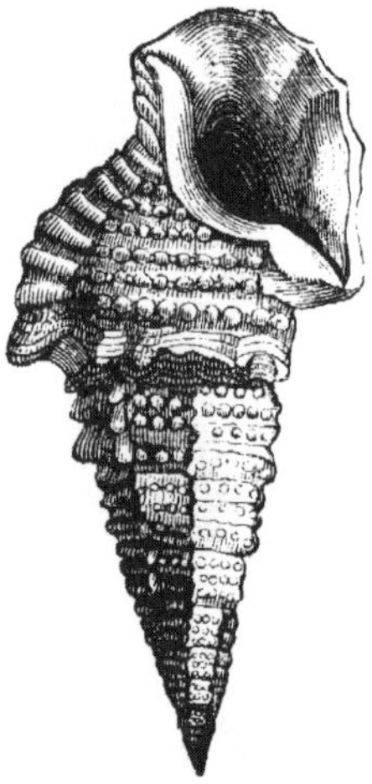

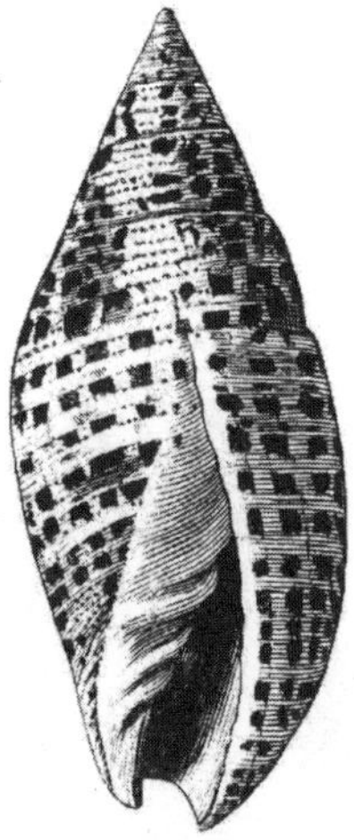

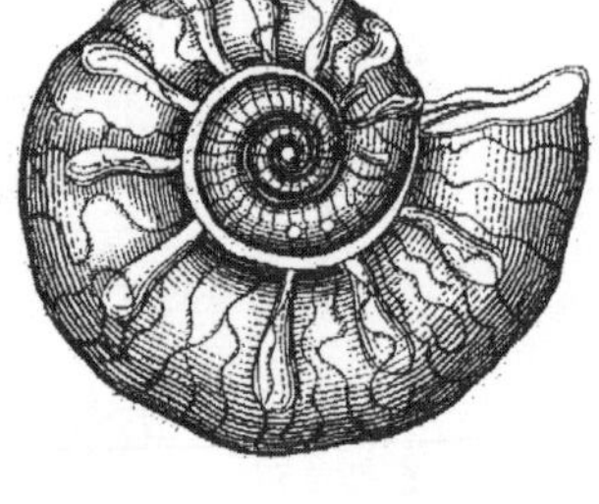

Name ______________________________ Date ________________

What Do You Remember? Lesson 9 Review Questions

1. What is the main difference between bivalves and gastropods?

2. How do bivalves filter feed and breathe?

3. Where are live clams found on shore?

4. How can you tell the age of a clam?

5. Which bivalves cling to rocks and other surfaces?

6. How and when do they find food?

7. Where are pearls found and how are they formed?

8. How do scallops swim?

9. What does the term "gastropod" mean?

10. What is a radula?

11. What is an operculum?

12. What kind of gastropod makes a shell that has a wide, pearly colored lip that flares outward?

13. What kind of gastropod has a shell with several large holes?

14. What kind of gastropod has no shell?

15. What do some nudibranchs do with the stingers of the sea anemones that they eat?

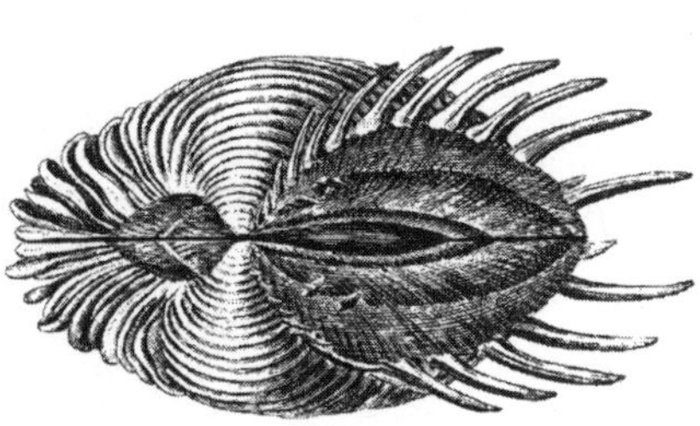

BIVALVES

Lesson 9

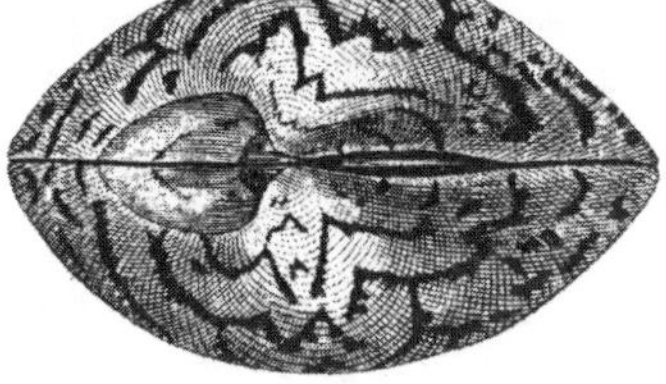

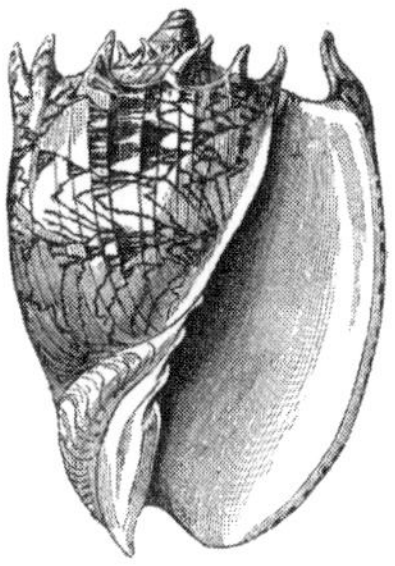

GASTROPODS

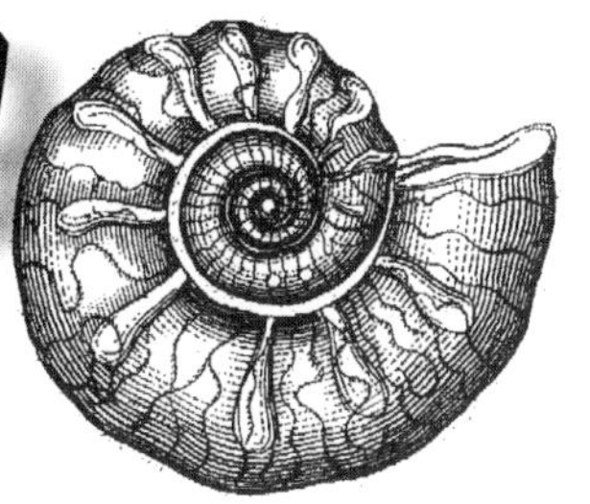

Lesson 9

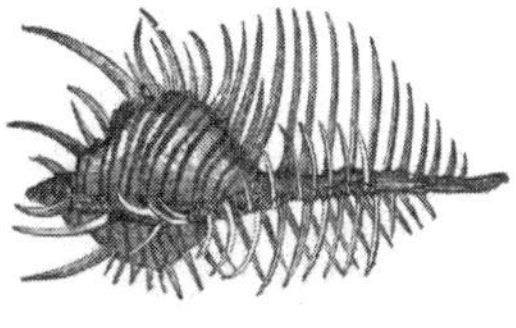

COPYWORK

There is the sea, vast and spacious, teeming with creatures beyond number-living things both large and small.

Psalm 104:25

COPYWORK

There is the sea, vast and
spacious, teeming with creatures
beyond number—living things both
large and small.

Psalm 104:25

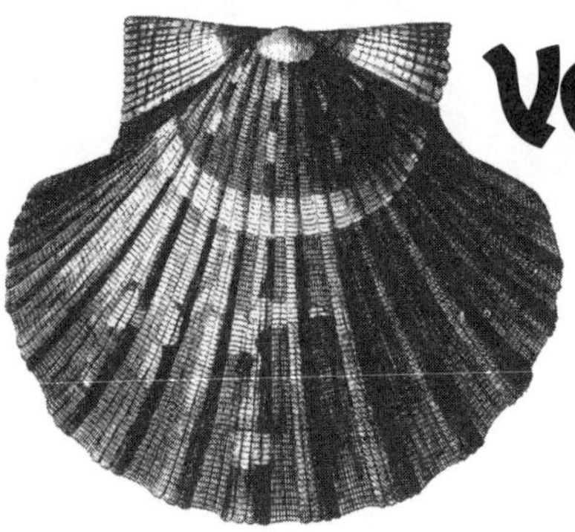

Vocabulary Crossword

Lesson 9

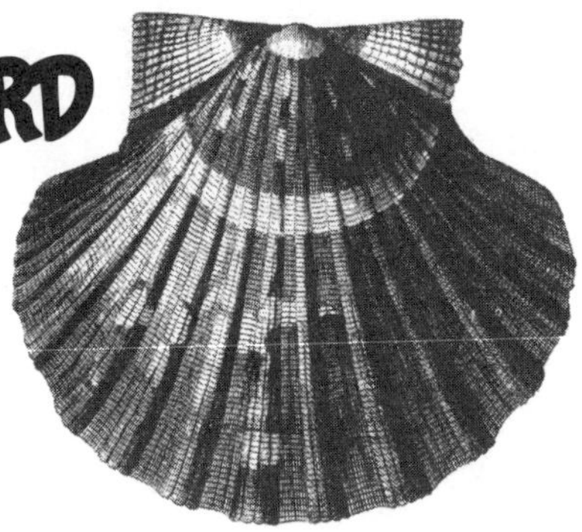

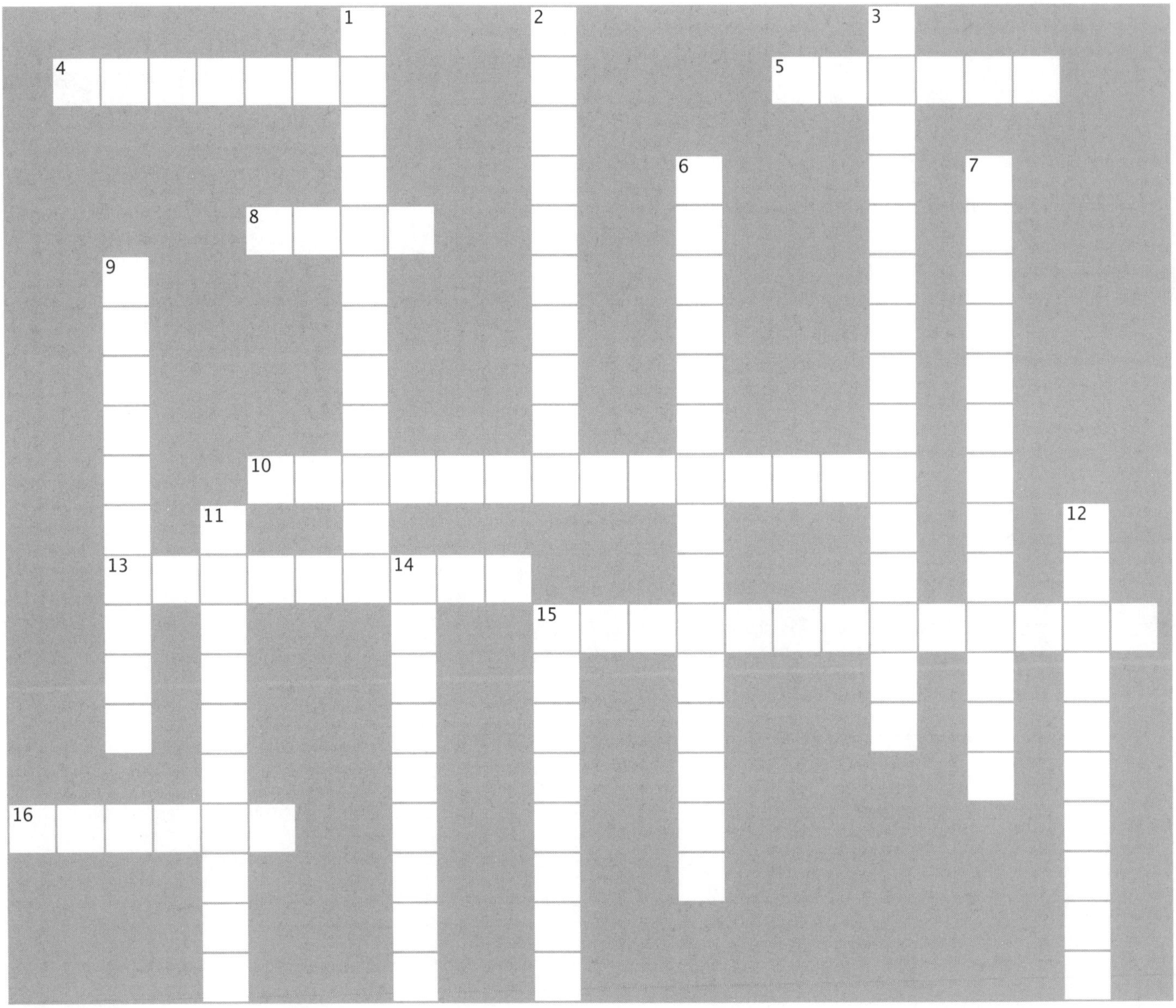

MANTLE	**GASTROPODS**	**BIVALVES**
SIPHON TUBE	**INCURRENT SIPHON**	**EXCURRENT SIPHON**
BYSSAL THREADS	**SPAT**	**CULTURED PEARLS**
RADULA	**CONCHOLOGY**	**PROBOSCIS**
NUDIBRANCH	**ABALONE**	**MOTHER OF PEARL**
CONE SHELL	**SEA WASH BALLS**	

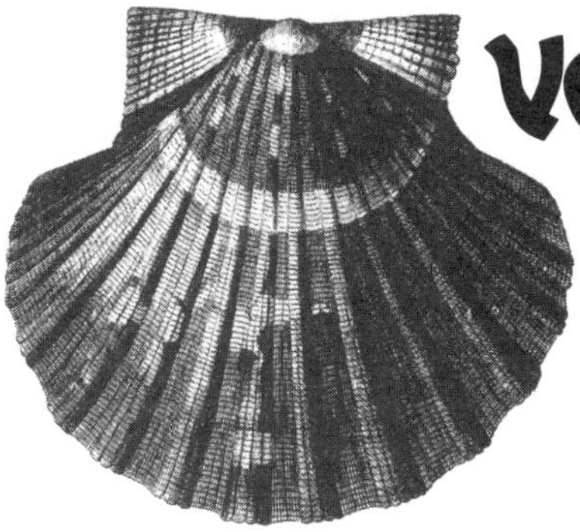

VOCABULARY CROSSWORD

LESSON 9

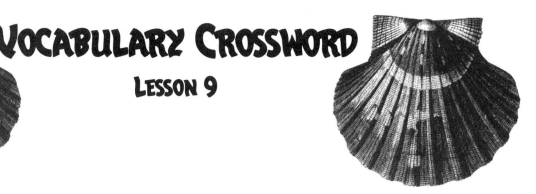

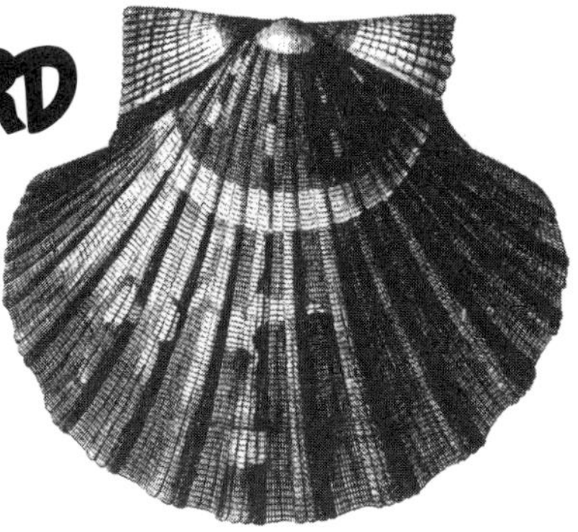

Across

4. An animal that clamps onto rocks and other surfaces in the deep waters of the Pacific Ocean. Its shell is unique with several holes running along the edge of the shell.
5. An organ inside a mollusk's body that converts calcium and other minerals into a shell.
8. What a mussel is known as in its larval stage.
10. Pearls that are purposely made by inserting a bead into the oyster to begin the process of making the pearl. TWO WORDS
13. A long stalk which includes the whelk's radula and mouth.
15. The tough fibers that mussels use to attach themselves to a spot. TWO WORDS
16. A gastropod's organ that resembles a jagged knife. It is used to scrape algae and drill holes in animal shells.

Down

1. Whelks' eggs that are papery and spongy masses and often wash up on the beach. THREE WORDS
2. The excurrent siphon, also called a _________ __________, is what bivalves use to expel wastes. TWO WORDS
3. The tube bivalves use to take in water. TWO WORDS
6. The tube bivalves use to expel wastes. TWO WORDS
7. The shiny inside lining of an abalone shell. THREE WORDS
9. A group of mollusks; its name means stomach-foot. Slugs and snails are in this group.
11. The study of shells.
12. A beautiful gastropod with colorful, frilly gills that come in many shapes and sizes. Its name means "naked gills."
14. One of the craftiest predators of the sea that can be very poisonous to people because of its venomous proboscis. TWO WORDS
15. A group of mollusks that has two shell halves. Mussels, scallops, cockles, oysters and clams are in this group.

MOLLUSKS MINIBOOKS

Lesson 9

Paste your Mollusks Miniature
Books onto this page.

DIVE DEEPER

Lesson 9

Dissect a Mollusk

Have you ever gotten an up close look at a mollusk? You can by dissecting one! Simply purchase a mollusk and dissection supplies from any science supplier and print up sheets from the Internet that detail how to dissect the animal.

You can find dissection supplies at many online stores. Some of them will also sell instructions and literature related to each animal you dissect. Here are a few stores that may have supplies for this dissection:

Hometrainingtools.com – Home Training Tools
nilesbio.com – Niles Biological Supply
Carolina.com – Carolina Biological Supply
Wardsci.com – Ward's Natural Sciences

Make A Mollusk Meal

If no one is allergic, make some mollusks for dinner! Here are some ideas:

Oyster Soup
Fried Oysters
New England Clam Chowder
Clam Fritters
Scalloped Clams
Clam Cakes
Baked Clams
Scallops (many recipes use scallops)

You can find recipes for the dishes listed above at www.cooks.com.

Book Suggestions

Pearlie Oyster: A Tale of an Amazing Oyster by Suzanne Tate. A living book about the amazing life of an oyster and how a pearl is formed.
Skippy Scallop: A Tale of Bright Blue Eyes by Suzanne Tate. The interesting story of an animal that survives because of its many blue eyes.
About Mollusks: A Guide for Children by Catherine Sill. This attractive title consists mainly of large, realistic watercolors, each accompanied by a sentence or two of simply written text. It concludes with a field guide containing extra data on the featured creatures.
Mollusks: Snails, Clams, and Their Relatives by Beth Blaxland. This book defines mollusks, such as land snails and pearl oysters, and describes their physical features, life cycles, habitats, senses, food, and means of self-defense.

*Be aware that some titles may contain evolutionary content

MY MOLLUSK PROJECT
Lesson 9

What I did:

What I learned:

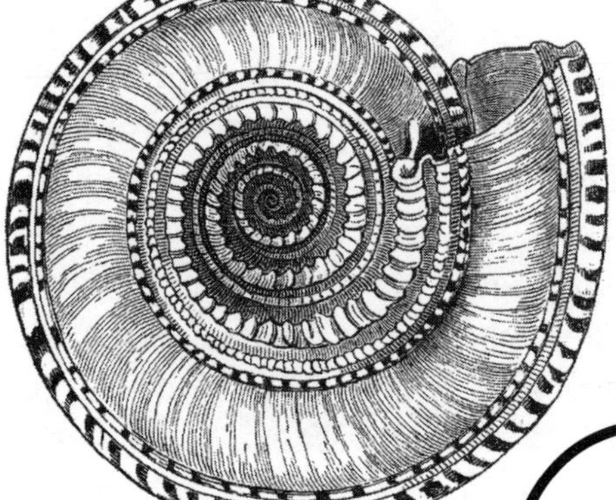

Scientific Speculation Sheet

Resonance

Lesson 9

Name____________________________ Date ______________

Materials Used:

Procedure:

Hypothesis:

Results:

Fascinating Facts

about

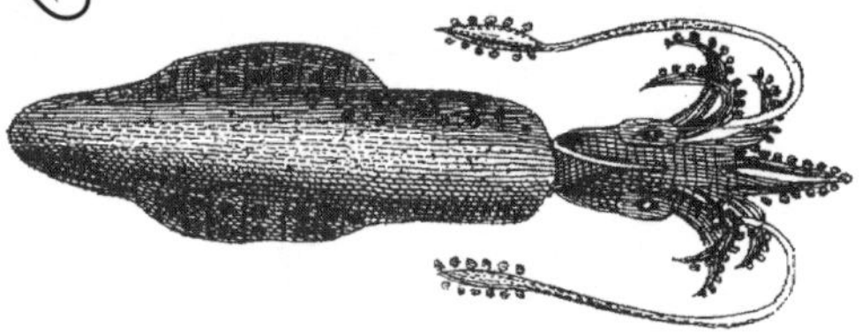

CEPHALOPODS

LESSON 10

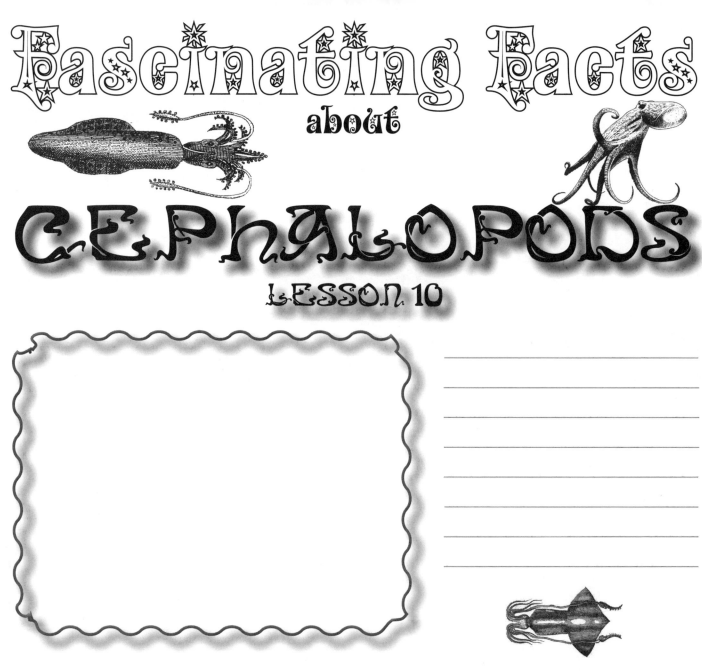

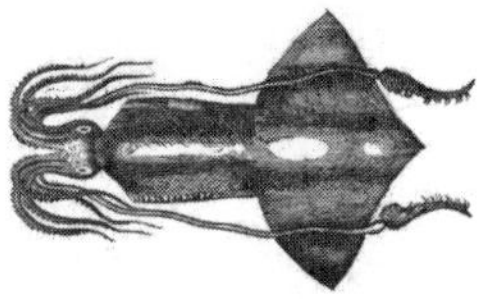

Name ____ Date ____________________

What Do You Remember?
Lesson 10 Review Questions

1. What does "cephalopod" mean?

2. What are the four different kinds of animals in the cephalopod group?

3. How do cephalopods swim?

4. What do cephalopods usually eat?

5. What kind of mouth do cephalopods have?

6. What are some of the defenses that cephalopods have?

7. What is the internal shell of the cuttlefish called?

8. How many arms do cuttlefish and squids have?

9. What does a squid usually do after it mates or lays eggs?

10. How many arms does an octopus have?

11. Why do scientists think octopuses are intelligent?

12. What is different about the nautilus compared to other cephalopods?

13. How does the nautilus move up and down in the water?

14. Describe a chiton.

15. Which land animal is it like and why?

16. How is it like a gastropod?

17. Where might you find a chiton during the day?

CUTTLEFISH

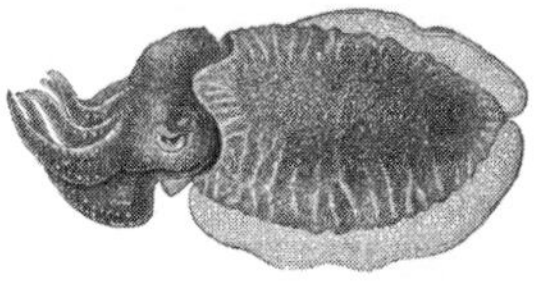

NAUTILUS

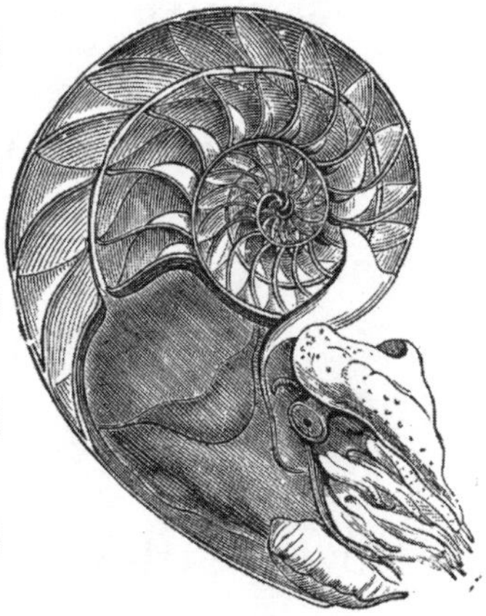

CHITON

SQUID

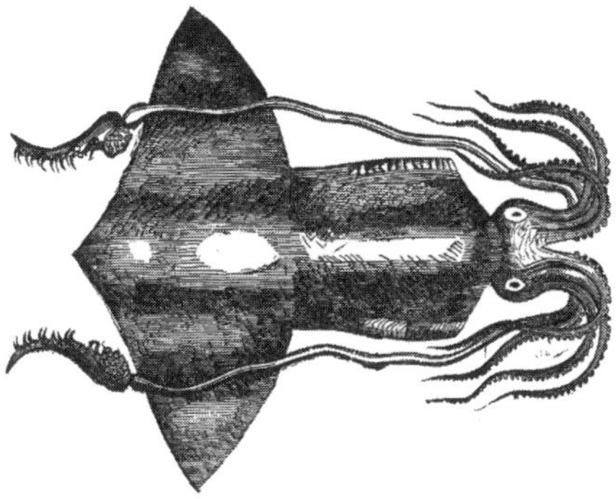

OCTOPUS

LESSON 10

SPERM WHALE ~ GIANT SQUID BATTLE

LESSON 10

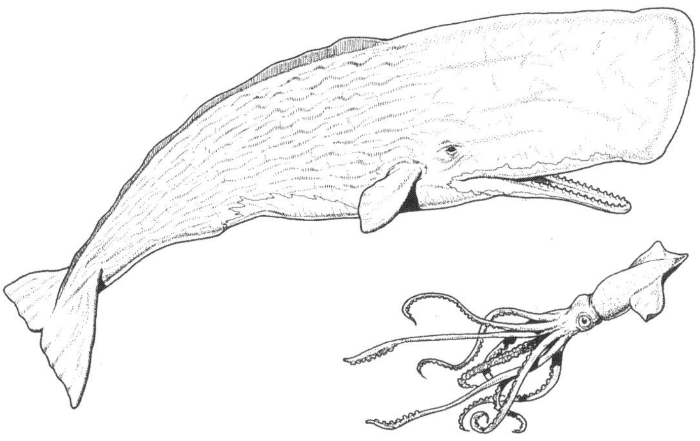

COPYWORK

All kinds of animals, birds, reptiles
and creatures of the sea are being
tamed and have been tamed by man,
but no man can tame the tongue.

James 3:7-8

COPYWORK

All kinds of animals, birds, reptiles and creatures of the sea are being tamed and have been tamed by man, but no man can tame the tongue.

James 3:7 -8

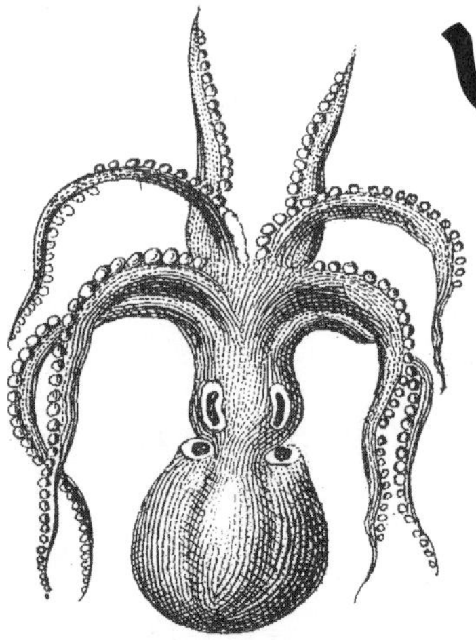

VOCABULARY CROSSWORD

LESSON 10

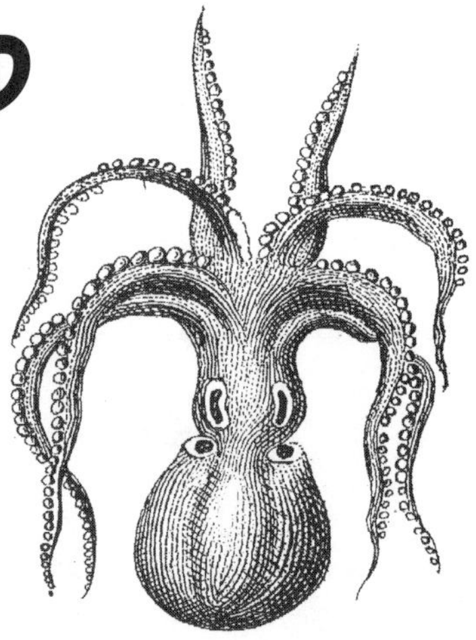

CEPHALOPODS
CUTTLEBONE
HYPONOME
CHITON
GIRDLE

JET PROPULSION
NAUTILUS
SHOAL
CUTTLEFISH
SQUID

CHROMATOPHORES
PHOTORECEPTORS
HOOD
OCTOPUS
CHAMBERED NAUTILUS

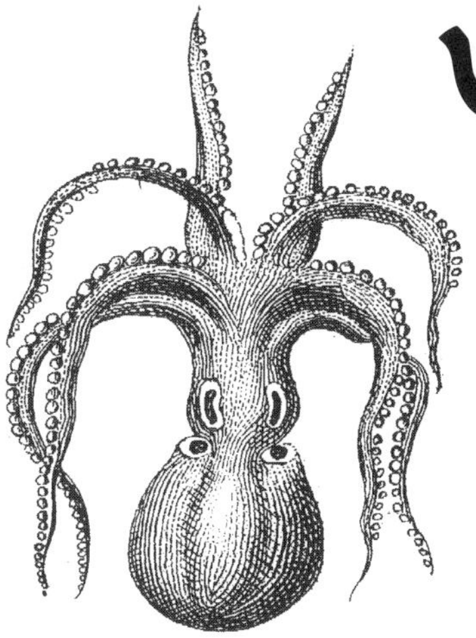

Vocabulary Crossword

Lesson 10

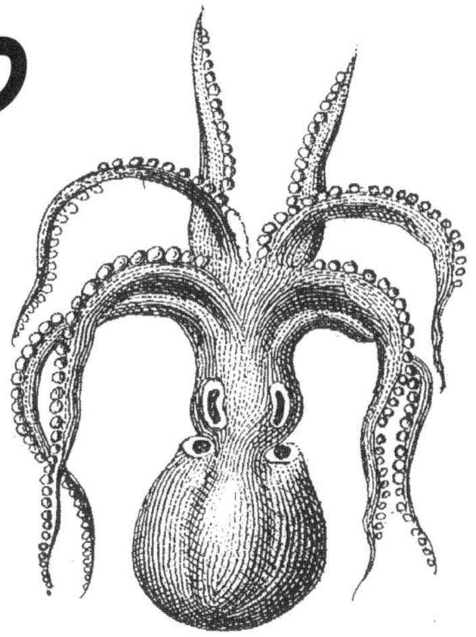

Across

5. The thickened area over the head of a nautilus.
8. The tube which the stream of water goes out of in jet propulsion.
11. The protruding portion of the chiton's mantle.
13. The parts that detect light in a human eye.
14. A cephalopod that rises and sinks due to gas-filled chambers in its shell. It can have anywhere between 38 and 90 arms.
15. A cephalopod with ten arms and a beak.

Down

1. A large, cream-colored cephalopod with brown, wavy lines and many arms. It is the only cephalopod that creates an external shell. TWO WORDS
2. Cells with pigments that can be manipulated to change the color of a cephalopod's skin, allowing it to blend into its surroundings.
3. The cephalopod's ability to allow water inside its body, then quickly squeeze it out, sending a jet stream out of its body and propelling it backward. TWO WORDS
4. A nocturnal cephalopod with eight arms and a beak. It lives in shallow waters, spending most of its time on the sea floor.
6. A group of squids.
7. A graceful animal that lives on the bottom of the ocean. It can quickly change its color and even its texture to match its surroundings. It has a shell on the inside of its body.
9. A group of mollusks. The name means head foot. The octopus, squid, nautilus and cuttlefish are in this group.
10. The internal shell of a cuttlefish.
12. A creature in the class polyplacophora. Eight plates make up its shell, and it has neither eyes nor arms.

CEPHALOPODS MINIBOOK

LESSON 10

Paste your Cephalopods Fan
onto this page.

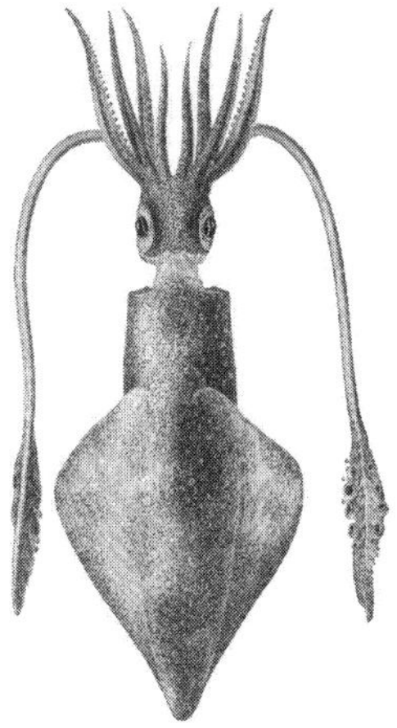

DIVE DEEPER

Lesson 10

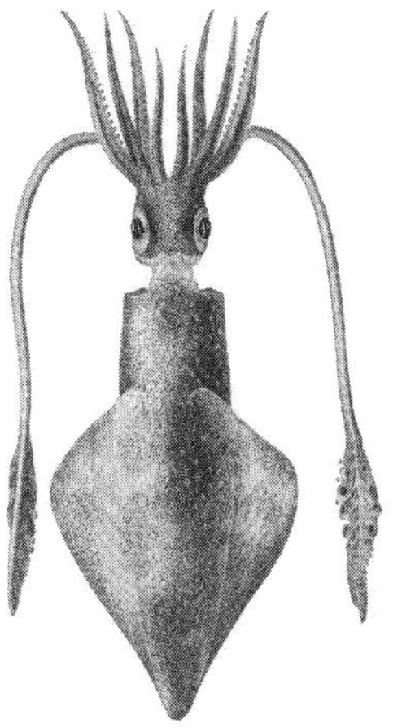

Dissect a Squid

Purchase a squid from a seafood or natural food store or a science supplier and find its beak and other parts!

You can find dissection supplies at many online stores. Some of them will also sell instructions and literature related to each animal you dissect. Here are a few stores that may have supplies for this dissection:

Hometrainingtools.com – Home Training Tools
nilesbio.com – Niles Biological Supply
Carolina.com – Carolina Biological Supply
Wardsci.com – Ward's Natural Sciences

My Favorite Cephalopod

Do some research to discover all the different kinds of cephalopods found in the ocean. Choose your favorite one and gather as much information about that particular cephalopod as you can. Be sure to study its scientific name, finding out what it means in English. Why was it given that name? After gathering your information, create a special fact page about your cephalopod. Enhance your page with colorful illustrations. You can create a book with your siblings or friends by putting everyone's cephalopod fact pages together.

Book and DVD Suggestions

Oozey Octopus: A Tale of a Clever Critter by Suzanne Tate. A living book with little known facts about a solitary, intelligent creature that surprises the scientific community.
Gentle Giant Octopus with audio: Read, listen and wonder by Karen Wallace. Poetical phrasing accompanied by the gentle, yet vividly compelling watercolor illustrations make this more than just an informational read. The picture book format will keep the interest of young children while presenting the facts about this lesser-known inhabitant of the sea. The audio provides a well-articulated narration; sound effects and background music enrich the telling.
Cephalopods: Octopuses, Squids, and Their Relatives by Beth Blaxland. Defines cephalopods, such as blue-ringed octopuses and giant squids, and describes their physical characteristics, life cycles, habitats, senses, food, and means of self-defense.
Giant Squid: Mystery of the Deep (All Aboard Science Reader: Station Stop 2) by Jennifer Dussling. The 25-foot squid hauled in by a fishing boat off the coast of New Zealand in December 1997 was one of the most amazing stories of that year! Here's a fascinating look at the giant squid, cephalopods in general, and the implications of this extra-ordinary discovery.
Cuttlefish - Kings of Camouflage (NOVA DVD). With stunning underwater footage and in-depth expert interviews, NOVA gets up close and personal with this astonishing brainy bunch.

*Be aware that some titles may contain evolutionary content

MY CEPHALOPOD PROJECT
LESSON 10

What I did:

What I learned:

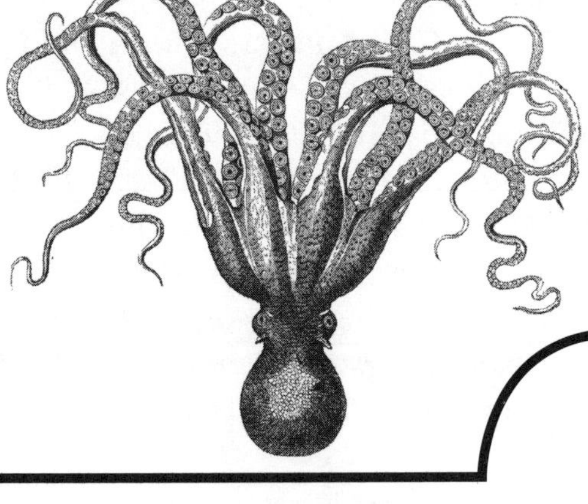

Scientific Speculation Sheet

Buoyancy

Lesson 10

Name____________________________ Date ______________

Materials Used:

Procedure:

Hypothesis:

Results:

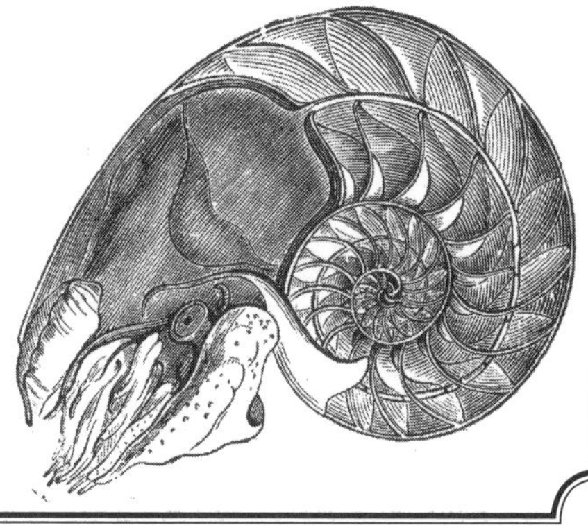

Fascinating Facts

about

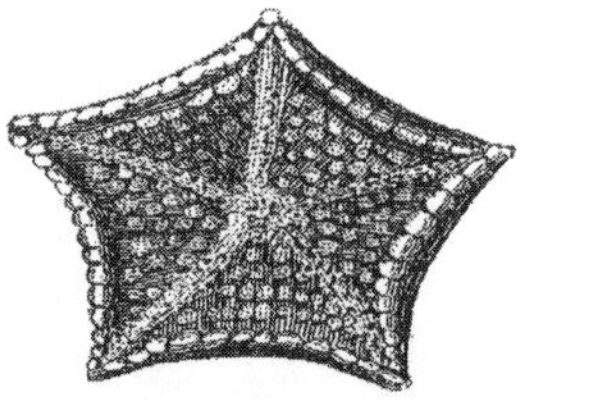

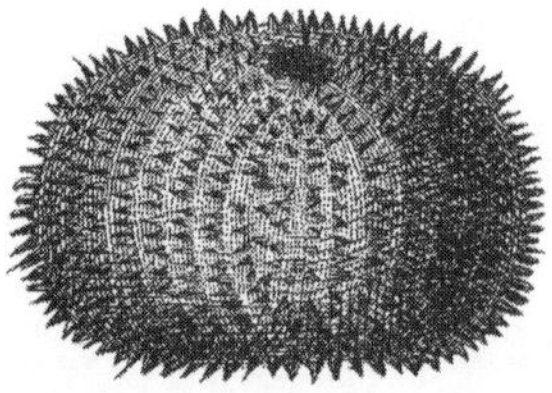

ECHINODERMS

LESSON 11

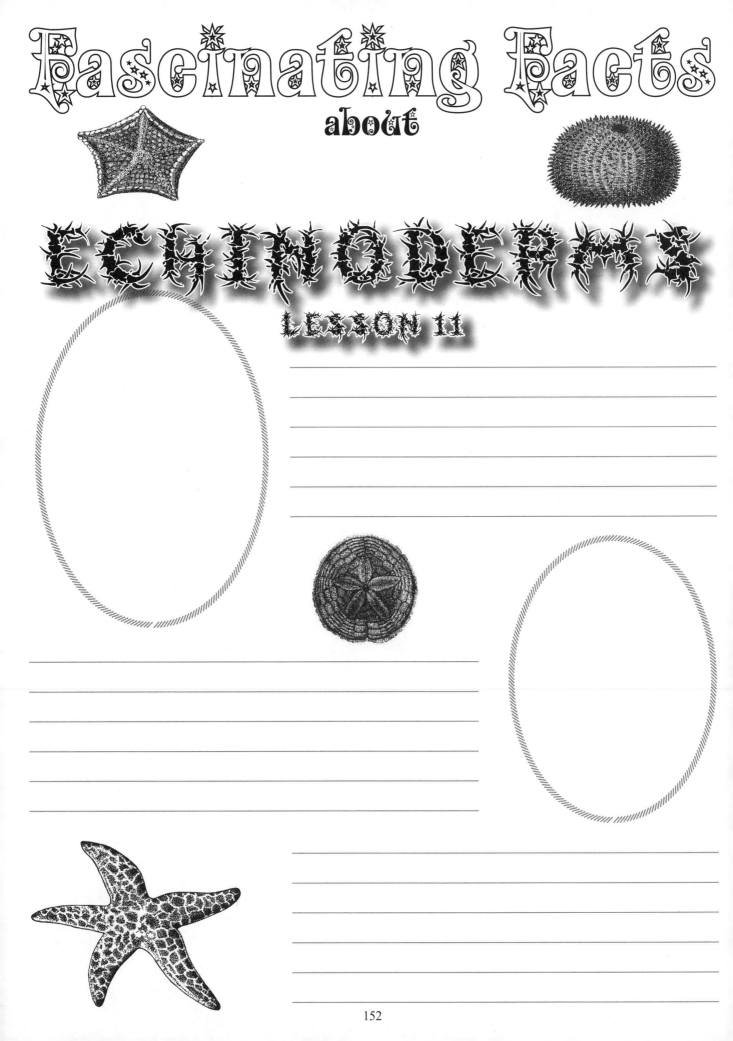

Fascinating Facts about

ECHINODERMS

LESSON 11

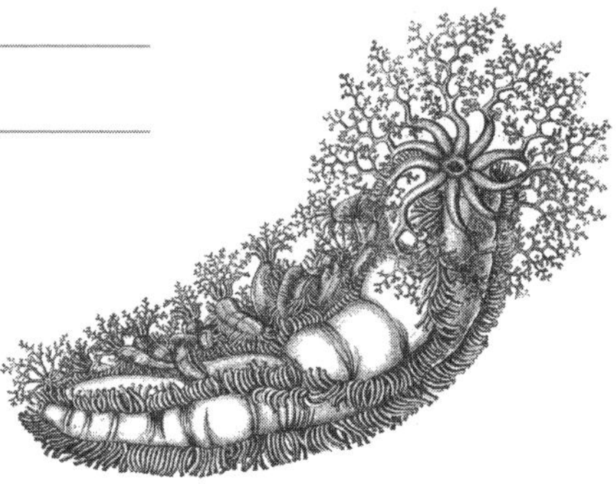

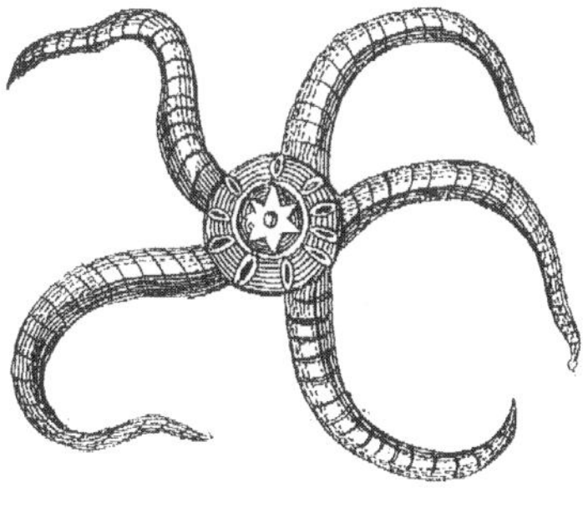

Name ______________________________ Date ______________

What Do You Remember? Lesson 11 Review Questions

1. What is the name of the phylum that includes sea stars, sand dollars, sea urchins and sea cucumbers?

2. What does phylum mean?

3. What is special about these animals' feet?

4. Explain how sea stars eat.

5. What is a sea star's favorite food?

6. What did clam fishermen once do to keep sea stars from eating the clams?

7. Why did this not work?

8. Why are brittle stars considered brittle?

9. How do they move across the ocean floor?

10. How is this different from sea stars?

11. What are sea urchins' teeth called?

12. What animal really likes to eat sea urchins?

13. Explain how a sand dollar eats.

14. How does a sea cucumber defend itself?

15. In what two ways do sea cucumbers eat?

ECHINODERMS

LESSON 11

SEA STARS

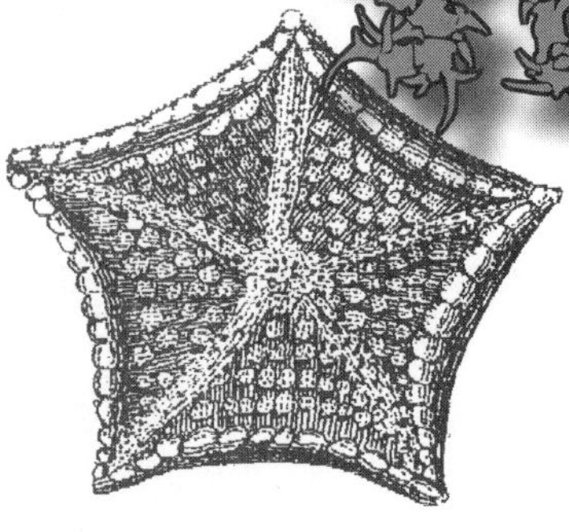

BRITTLE STARS

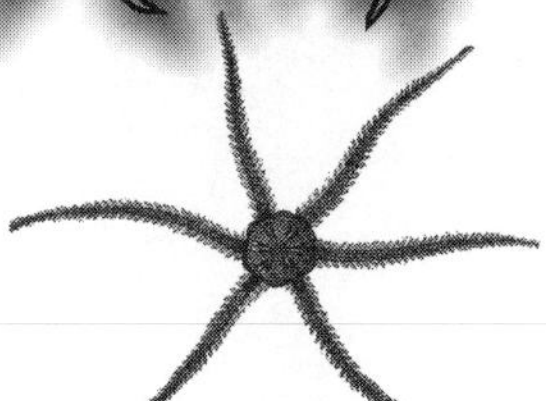

CRINOIDS

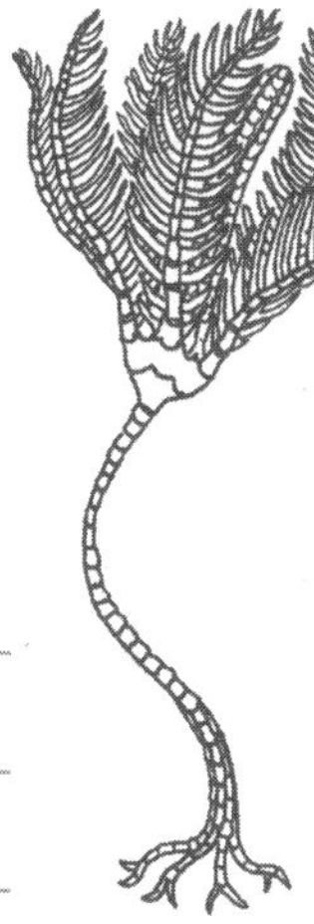

SEA URCHINS

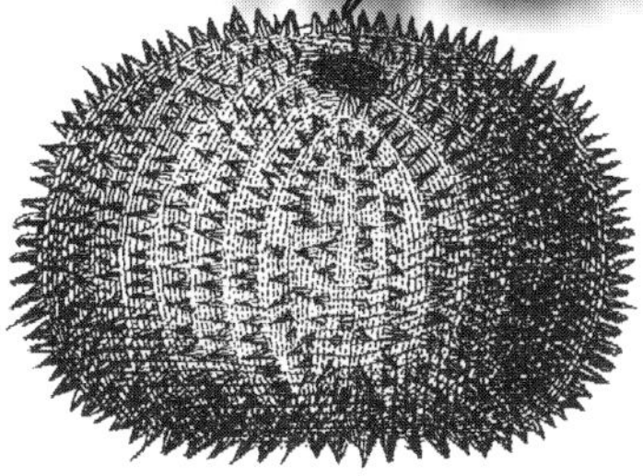

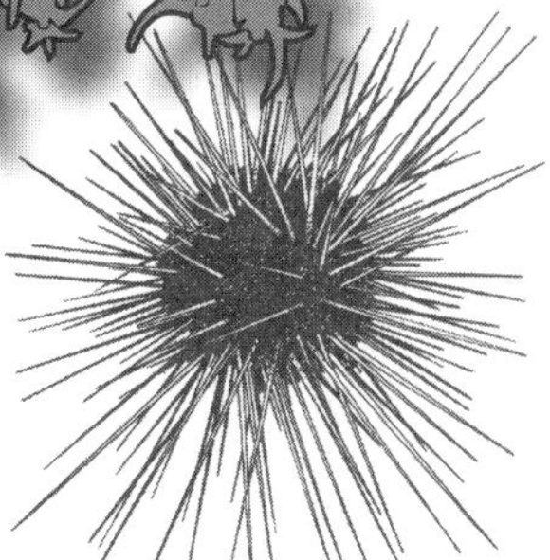

SAND DOLLARS

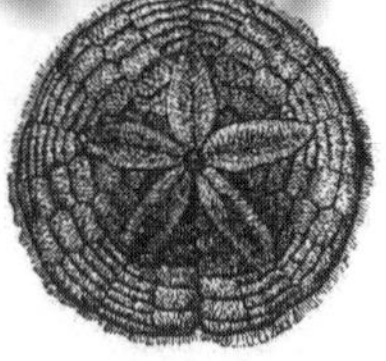

SEA CUCUMBERS

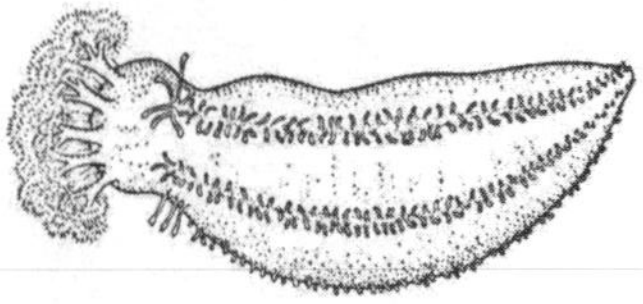

Legend of the Sand Dollar

Lesson 11

COPYWORK

Mightier than the thunder of the great waters, mightier than the breakers of the sea—the LORD on high is mighty.

Psalm 93:4

COPYWORK

Mightier than the thunder of the great
waters, mightier than the breakers
of the sea–the LORD on high is
mighty.

Psalm 93:4

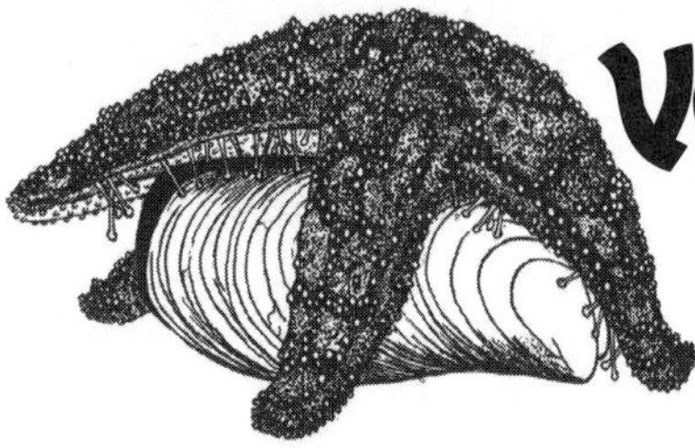

VOCABULARY CROSSWORD

LESSON 11

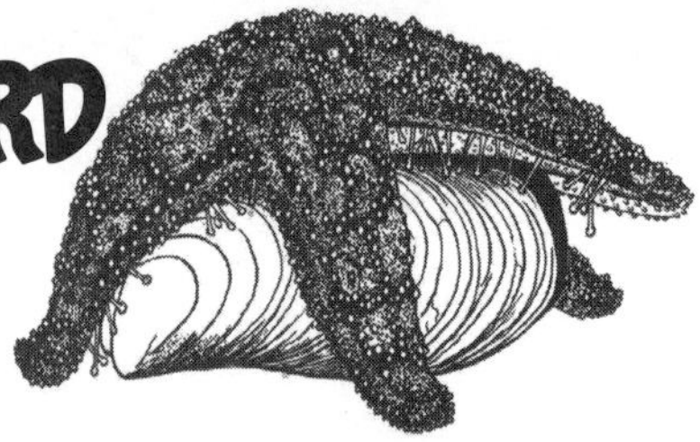

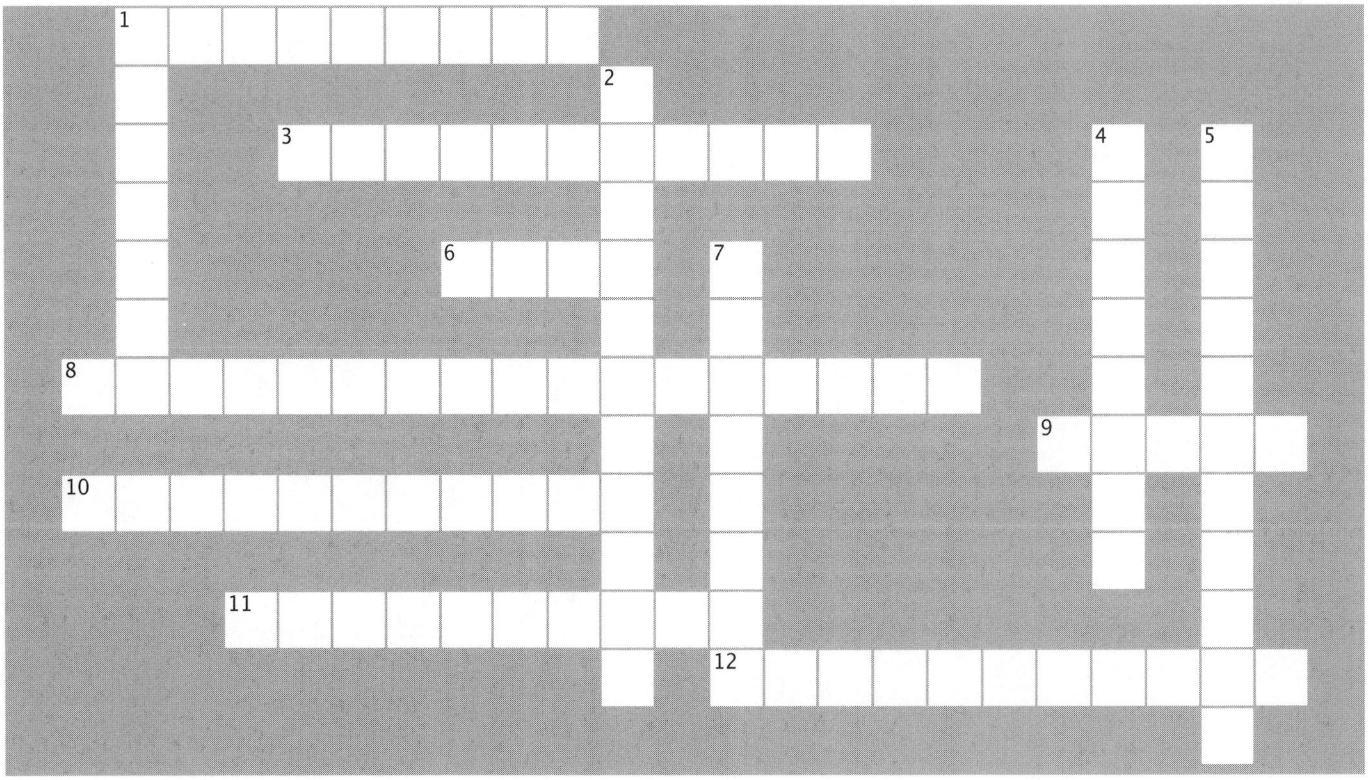

ECHINODERMS
BRITTLE STAR
PINNULES
TEST
FOOD GROOVES

SEA STAR
CRINOIDS
CIRRI
SEA CUCUMBER

REGENERATE
FEATHER STAR
SEA URCHIN
ARISTOTLE'S LANTERN

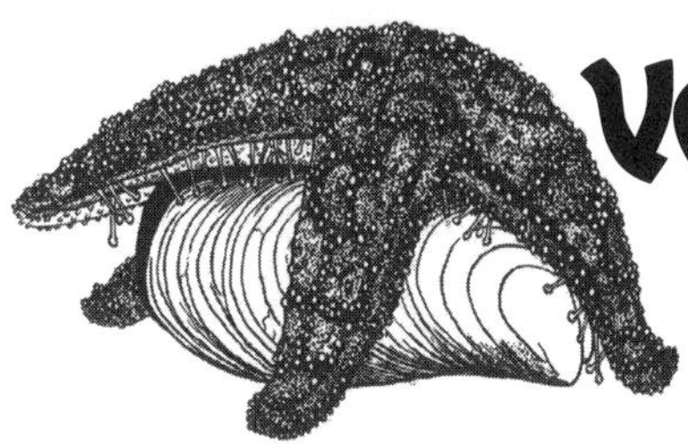

Vocabulary Crossword

Lesson 11

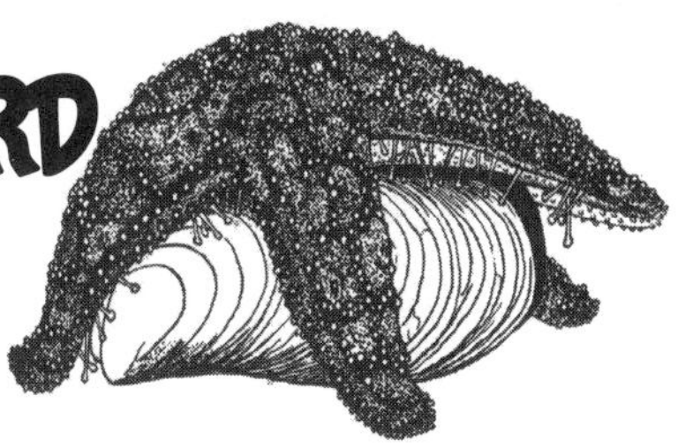

Across

1. A creature with no arms that is completely covered in spines. TWO WORDS
3. A creature with a mouth (surrounded by many feathery tentacles) that faces upward toward the surface of the ocean. TWO WORDS
6. A rounded body under the spine of a sea urchin. It can be seen when a sea urchin dies and loses its spine.
8. The name of the system in which the sea urchin's five special teeth are arranged. TWO WORDS
9. A crinoid's feelers.
10. Creatures with spiny skin and tube feet, having no eyes or brain. Sea urchins, sand dollars and starfish are in this group.
11. To re-grow parts of the body in order to recreate it as it was before.
12. A sausage-shaped benthic animal that has five rows of tube feet stretching the length of its body, enabling it to slowly move around the ocean floor. TWO WORDS

Down

1. An echinoderm found all over the ocean. It typically has five arms radiating out from a central disk and pushes its stomach out of its mouth to digest its prey. TWO WORDS
2. A fast-moving, sea star-looking creature with long, thin, fragile, snake-like arms surrounding a central disk. TWO WORDS
4. Creatures that have feathery arms on top of cup-shaped bodies and are commonly called sea lilies and feather stars.
5. These make up the star pattern found on the underside of a sand dollar. TWO WORDS
7. Feather star arms.

ECHINODERMS MINIBOOK

LESSON 11

Paste your Echinoderms
Pocket onto this page.

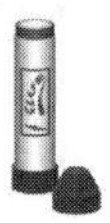

DIVE DEEPER

Lesson 11

Dissect a Sea Star

How would you like to get an up close look at a sea star? You can by dissecting one!

You can find dissection supplies at many online stores. Some of them will also sell instructions and literature related to each animal you dissect. Here are a few stores that may have supplies for this dissection:

Hometrainingtools.com – Home Training Tools
nilesbio.com – Niles Biological Supply
Carolina.com – Carolina Biological Supply
Wardsci.com – Ward's Natural Sciences

Sea Star Story

Write a story from the perspective of a starfish, detailing what happened when the oystermen tried to eliminate starfishes from the ocean. You can do this by creating a picture book or a story book.

My Favorite Echinoderm

Do some research to discover all the different kinds of echinoderms found in the ocean. Choose your favorite one and gather as much information about that particular echinoderm as you can. Be sure to study its scientific name, finding out what it means in English. Why was it given that name? After gathering your information, create a special fact page about your echinoderm. Enhance your page with colorful illustrations. You can create a book with your siblings or friends by putting everyone's echinoderm fact pages together.

Book Suggestions

Spiny Sea Star: A Tale of Seeing Stars by Suzanne Tate. A living book about a spiny-skinned animal (known also as a starfish) that is a marvel of nature.

Sea Stars, Sea Urchins, and Their Relatives: Echinoderms by Beth Blaxland. Defines echinoderms, such as sand dollars and crown-of-thorns sea stars, and describes their physical characteristics, life cycles, habitats, senses, food, and means of self-defense.

*Be aware that some titles may contain evolutionary content

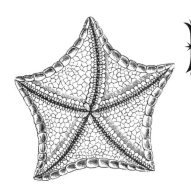

MY ECHINODERMS PROJECT

LESSON 11

What I did:

What I learned:

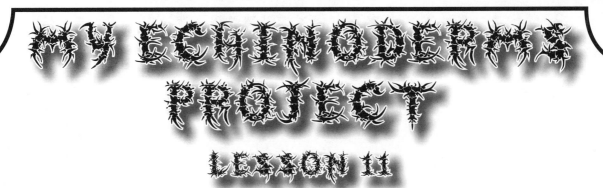

Fascinating Facts about

Cnidarians

Lesson 12

Name ______________________________ Date ______________

What Do You Remember? Lesson 12 Review Questions

1. What does "cnidaria" mean?

2. Where is the mouth on a cnidarian?

3. Explain how nematocysts work.

4. What is the difference between a polyp and a medusa?

5. Why are jellyfish considered plankton?

6. What is special about the box jelly?

7. What is special about the man-of-war?

8. How do sea anemones and corals differ from jellyfish?

9. How do corals differ from sea anemones?

10. Where do corals grow and why?

11. Explain how corals are dependent on algae.

12. What is the difference between stony coral and soft coral?

Jellyfish

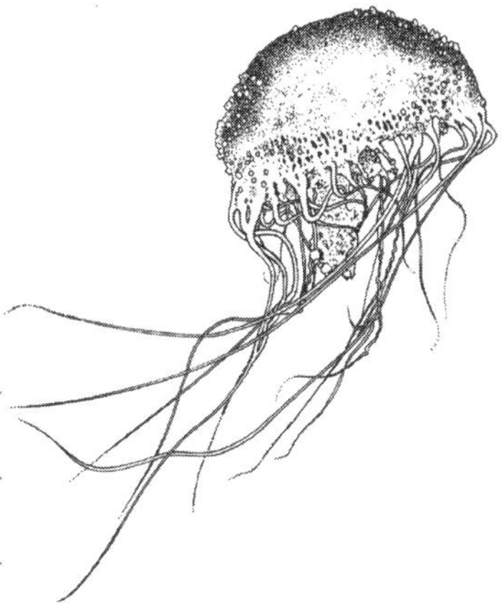

Sea Anemones

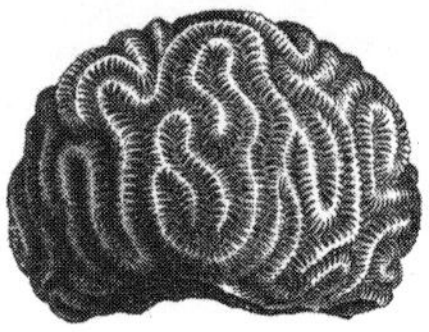

CORALS

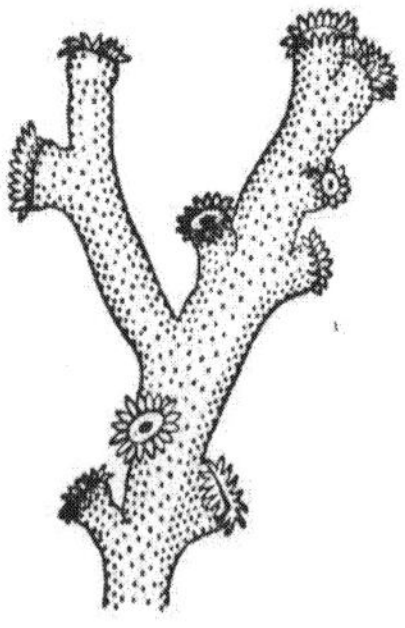

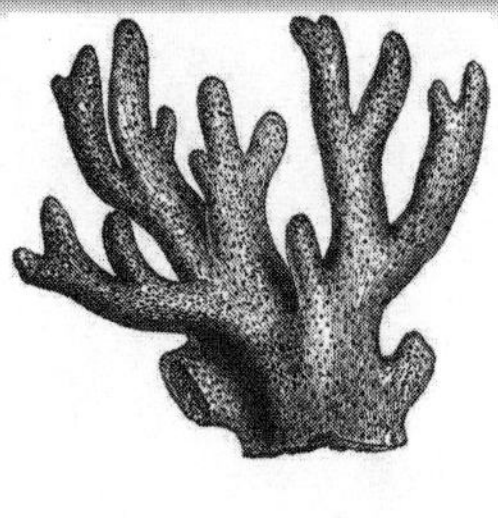

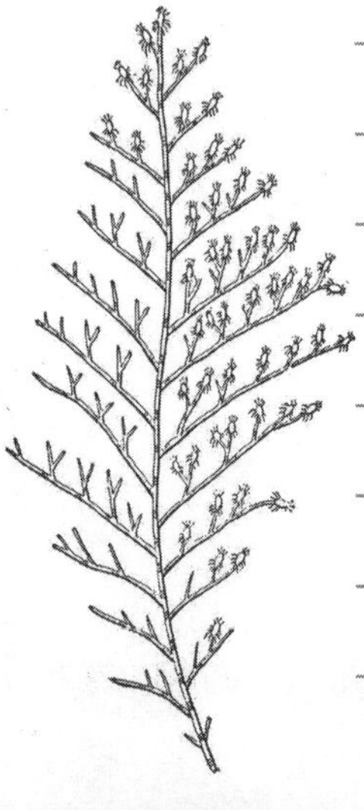

Great Barrier Reef

Lesson 12

COPYWORK

No mention shall be made of coral, or of pearls: for the price of wisdom is above rubies.

Job 28:18

COPYWORK

No mention shall be made of coral, or of pearls: for the price of wisdom is above rubies.

Job 28:18

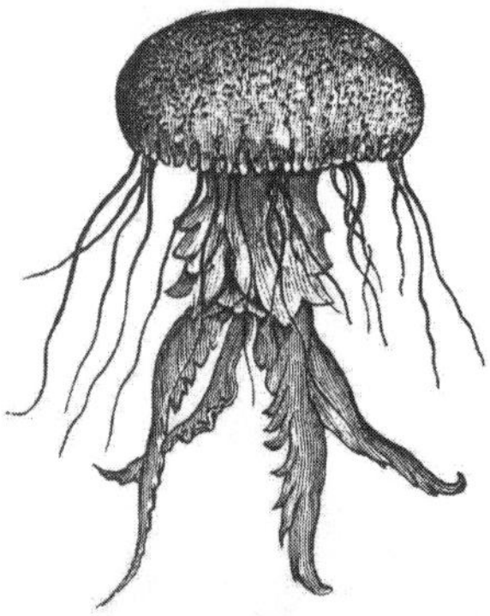

VOCABULARY CROSSWORD

LESSON 12

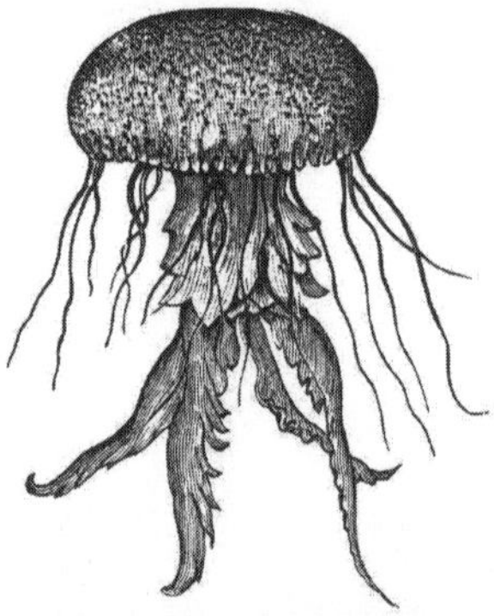

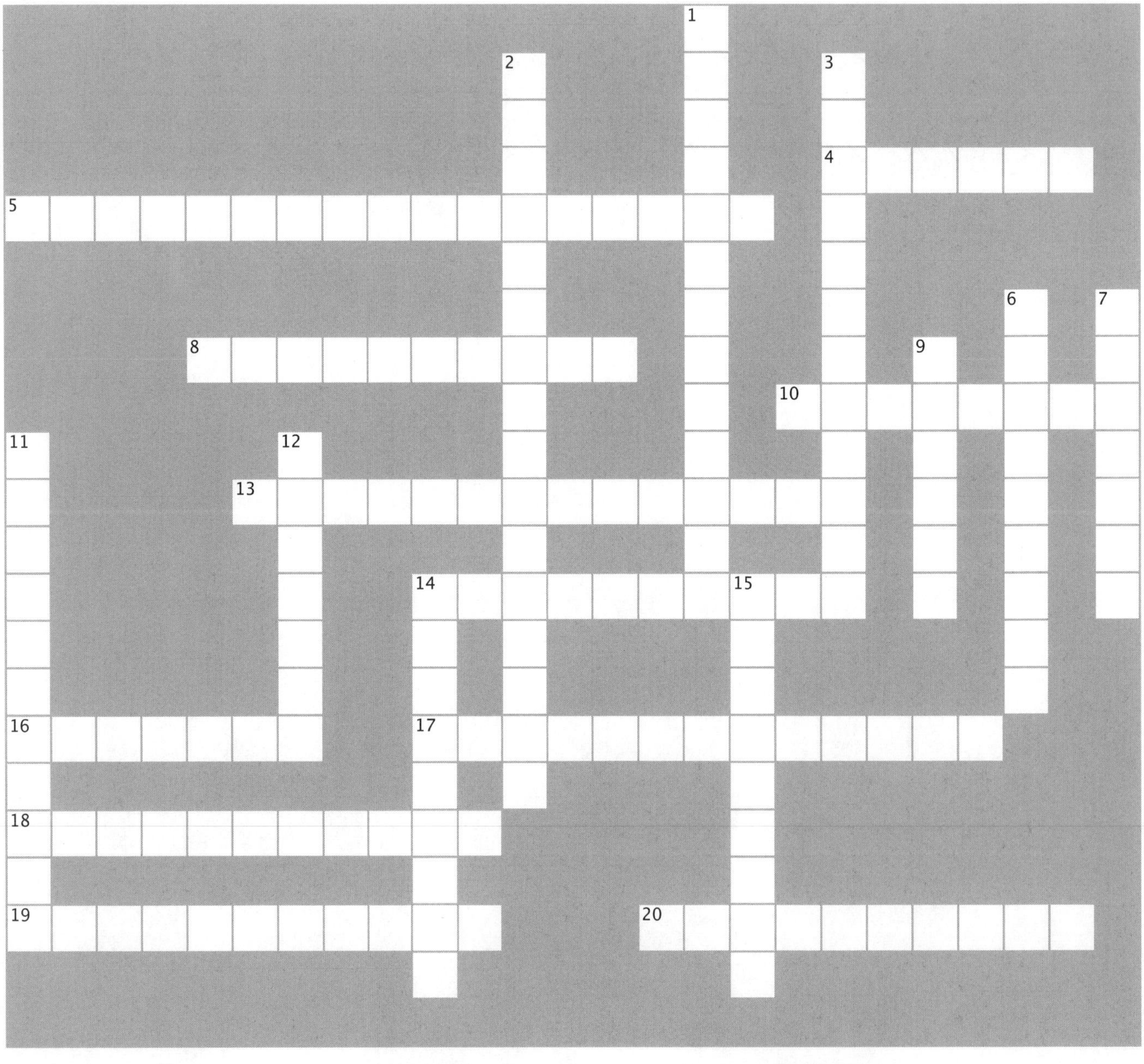

CNIDARIANS
NEMATOCYSTS
EPIDERMIS
SMACKS
SEA ANEMONES
STONY CORALS
ZOOXANTHELLAE

POLYPS
CAPSULE
GASTRODERMIS
JELLYFISH BLOOM
CORAL REEFS
SOFT CORALS
COMB JELLY

MEDUSAE
JELLYFISH
MESOGLEA
PLANULA
PORTUGUESE MAN-O-WAR
BLEACHED CORAL
GREAT BARRIER REEF

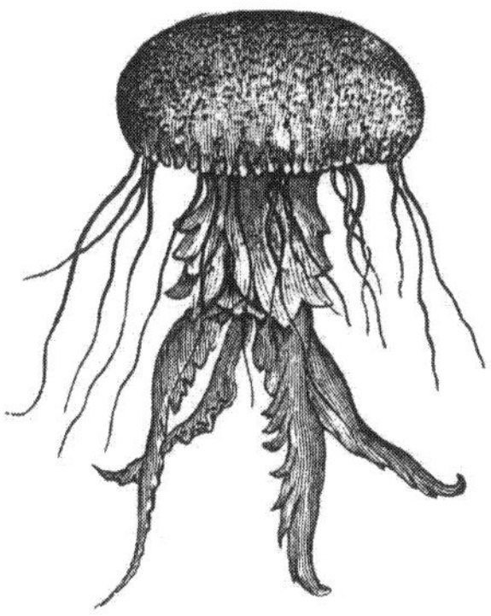

Vocabulary Crossword

Lesson 12

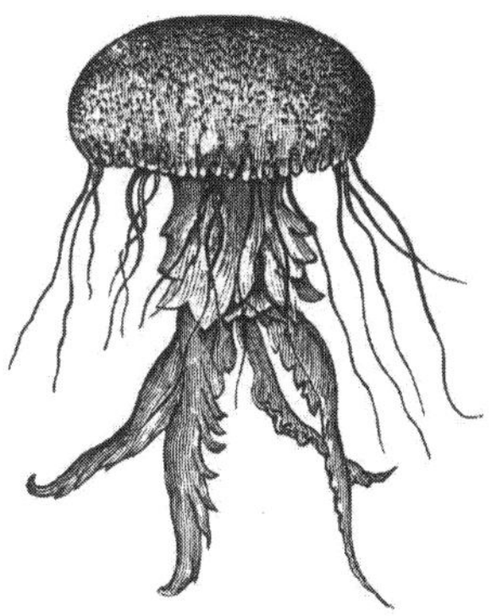

Across

4. Swarms of jellyfish.
5. A colony of hundreds of jelly-like creatures all linked together, making it appear to be just one creature. TWO WORDS
8. Corals that are soft and can be easily mistaken for plants. TWO WORDS
10. The jellylike substance in between the epidermis and the gastrodermis of a cnidarian.
13. What we call a very large smack of jellyfish. TWO WORDS
14. Large coral formations resulting from many corals gathered together building skeletons around themselves. TWO WORDS
16. The lid to a nematocyst's "jar" that can spring open.
17. Coral that has lost its color because the zooxanthellae in the coral has died. TWO WORDS
18. Cnidarians that are often thought of as plants and called the "flowers of the sea." TWO WORDS
19. Corals that build hard skeletons around themselves. These are the reef-building corals. TWO WORDS
20. Nettle-like animals that possess a powerful sting. Jellyfish, sea anemones and corals are examples of these creatures.

Down

1. Tiny phytoplankton that get captured by coral polyps. They provide nutrients and color for the polyps.
2. The largest coral reef, located near Australia. THREE WORDS
3. The inner layer of the cnidarian skin.
6. Cnidarians that are zooplankton and do not swim but simply float in the water.
7. The larval form of a jellyfish.
9. Cnidarians that have waving tentacles.
11. The stinging cells of a cnidarian that typically cover each tentacle.
12. Cnidarians that have dangling tentacles.
14. A non-nettle jellyfish that has no sting. Instead, it has a sticky substance on its tentacles to capture prey. TWO WORDS
15. The outer layer of the skin.

Cnidarians Minibook

Lesson 12

Paste your Cnidarians Flap Book onto this page.

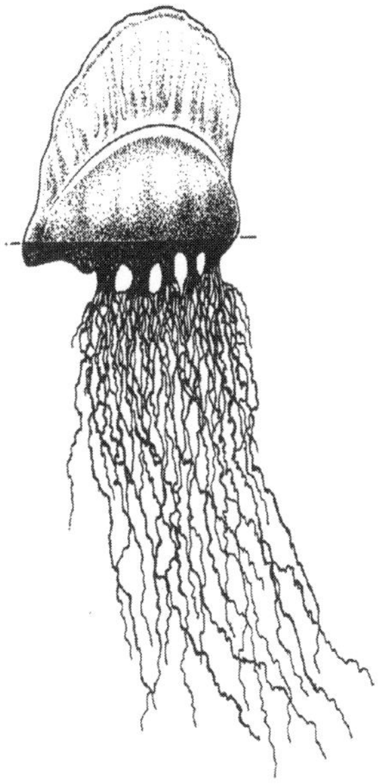

DIVE DEEPER

Lesson 12

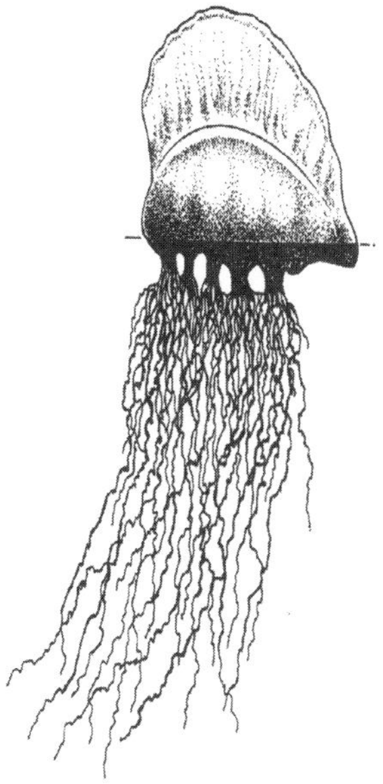

Write an Animal Report

Choose one of the reports from below:

Stinging Animals: Research all the animals in God's Kingdom that use stinging as a defense. Write a report and include images of all these creatures.

Dangerous Animals of Australia: You have learned that some of the most dangerous animals in the animal kingdom reside in one area, Australia. Research more about these creatures and write a report on the dangerous animals of Australia.

Favorite Sea Creature: Choose one of the families of animals you have studied and write a report about why you like this animal group the most.

Book and DVD Suggestions

Jenny Jellyfish: A Tale of Wiggly Jellies by Suzanne Tate. A living book with amazing facts about moon jellies and animals with no heart, bones or brain.

Jellyfish (Welcome Books) by Lloyd G. Douglas. Beautiful full-color photographs and simple text introduce young readers to jellyfish.

Night of the Moon Jellies by Mark Sasha. A charming living book about a boy who discovers a moon jelly on the beach.

Animals Without Backbones (DVD) by Phoenix Learning Group. As the camera surveys numerous underwater creatures, the narrator introduces the animals' characteristics, body structures and habitats. Fascinating details of jellyfishes, sea anemones, starfishes, squids, octopuses, and various insects reveal the diversity of invertebrates.

*Be aware that some titles may contain evolutionary content

My Cnidarian Project

Lesson 12

What I did:

What I learned:

Scientific Speculation Sheet

Currents

Lesson 12

Name____________________________ Date ______________

Materials Used:

Procedure:

Hypothesis:

Results:

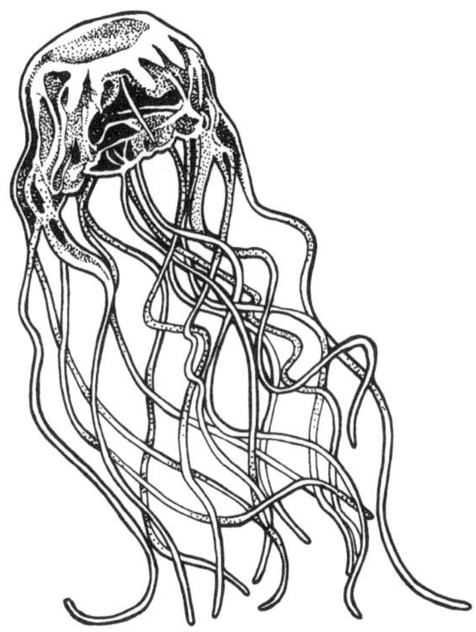

Fascinating Facts about

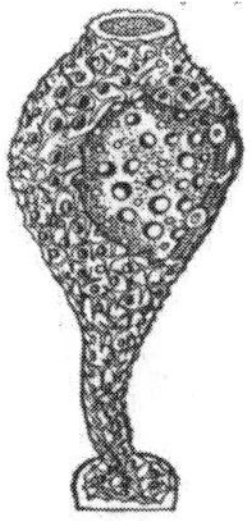

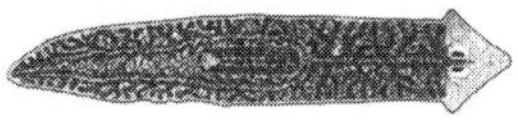

OTHER AQUATIC ANIMALS

LESSON 13

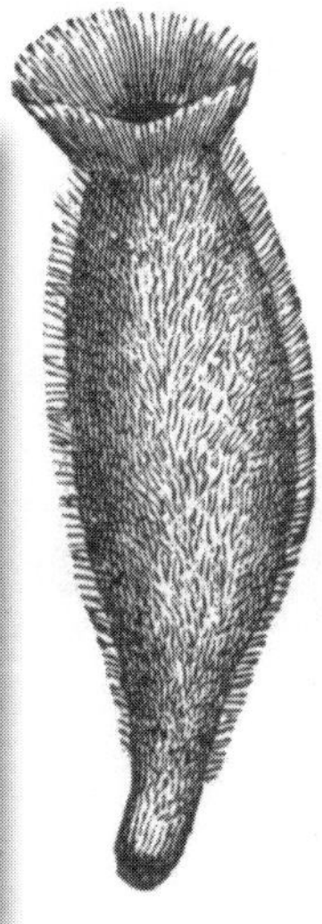

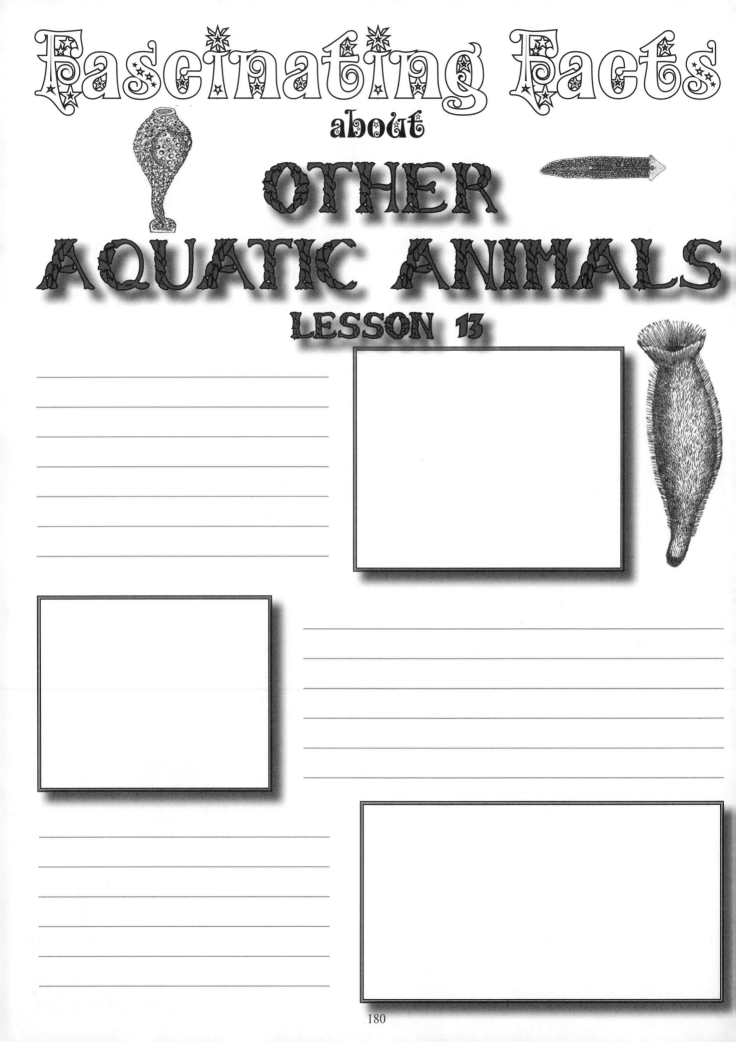

Fascinating Facts

about

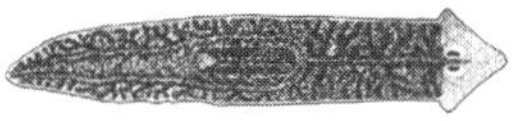

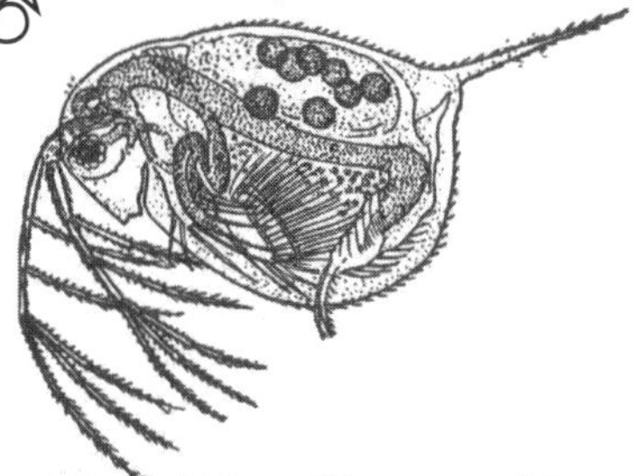

OTHER AQUATIC ANIMALS

LESSON 13

Name ______________________________ Date ______________

What Do You Remember? Lesson 13 Review Questions

1. How do scientists decide if a strange-looking creature is an animal?

2. What do sponges do for the water environment around them?

3. What are the ostia in a sponge?

4. What is the osculum of a sponge?

5. Why do some animals have features that are similar to those of other animals?

6. For what are the bristle worm's bristles used?

7. How do leeches eat?

8. Why do some marine flatworms look like nudibranchs?

9. How do rotifers eat?

10. Why are they called rotifers?

11. What are water bears called?

12. Why can water bears and rotifers be found in so many bodies of water?

SPONGES
LESSON 13

WATER WORMS
LESSON 13

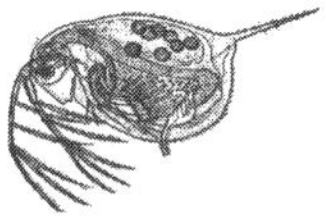

MICROSCOPIC ANIMALS

COPYWORK

The earth is the LORD's and everything in it, the world, and all who live in it; for he founded it upon the seas and established it upon the waters.

Psalm: 24:1-2

COPYWORK

The earth is the LORD's and everything in it, the world, and all who live in it; for he founded it upon the seas and established it upon the waters.

Psalm 24:1 -2

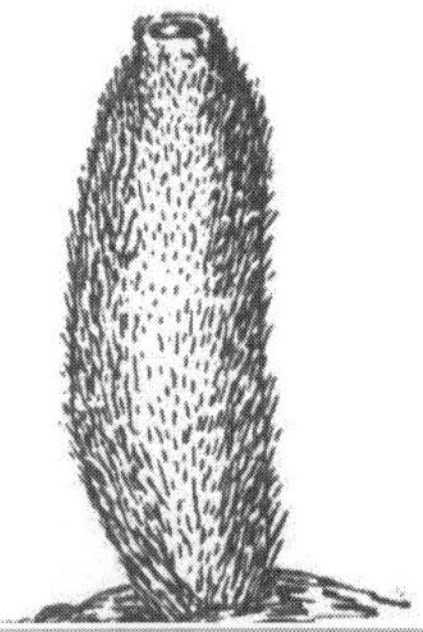

VOCABULARY CROSSWORD

LESSON 13

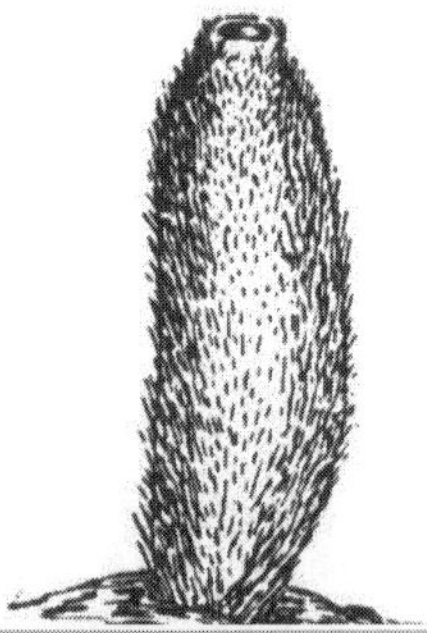

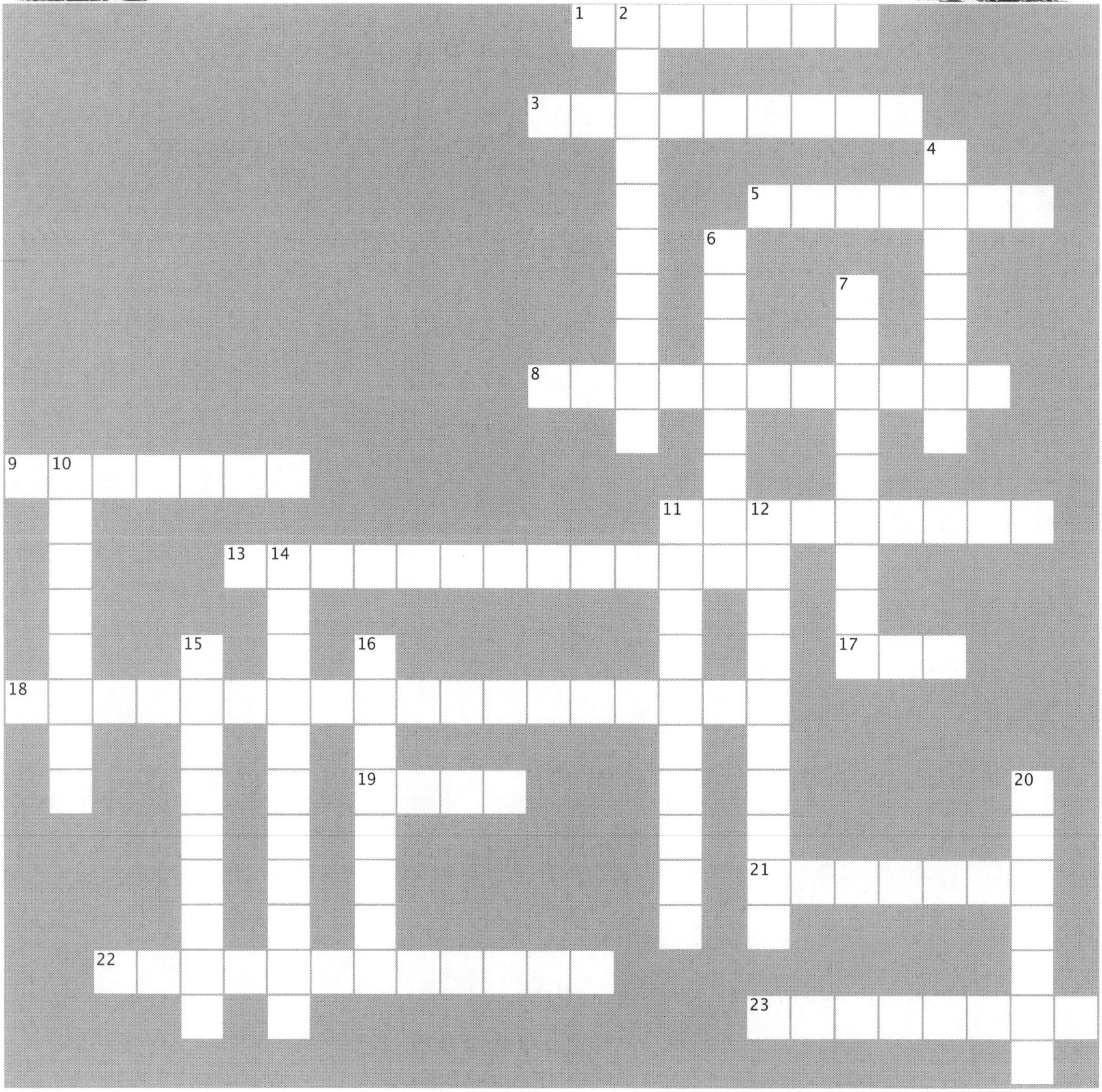

CELL
CONSUMERS
SPICULES
ATRIAL SIPHON
MIMICRY
RAGWORM
PORIFERA
PLANARIANS

MULTICELLULAR
PRODUCERS
SEA SQUIRT
ANNELIDA
LUGWORM
ROTIFER
OSCULUM
TUN

UNICELLULAR
SPONGES
ORAL SIPHON
TUBEWORM
MICROSCOPIC ANIMALS
PINACODERM
TUNICATES
TARDIGRADES

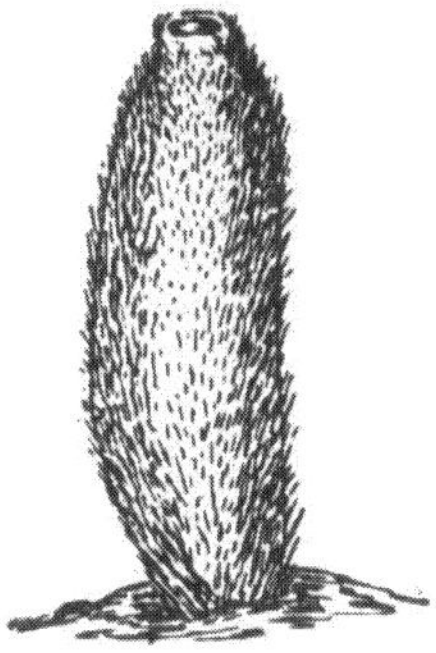

Vocabulary Crossword

Lesson 13

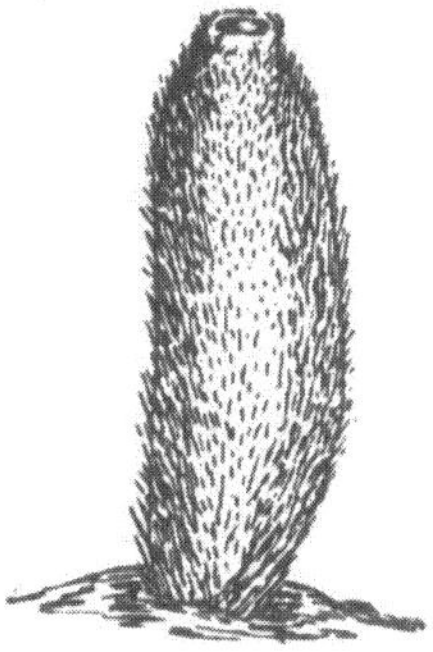

Across

1. Sessile creatures that come in all different shapes and sizes and are filter feeders in the ocean.
3. Another name for sea squirts.
5. A kind of bristle worm that makes little mounds of sand on the seashore.
8. Another name for water bears, because they are slow walkers and resemble bears under a microscope.
9. A kind of bristle worm that lives in burrows on the seashore.
11. Organisms (such as plants) that produce their own food.
13. When something is made up of many cells.
17. A state of being that a rotifer will go into to survive if the water dries up.
18. Animals that cannot be seen without a microscope. TWO WORDS
19. The basic unit of a living creature.
21. The large hole in a sponge where clean, filtered water exits.
22. One of the sea squirt's openings that spits water out of the animal. TWO WORDS
23. A kind of bristle worm that builds tubes around itself using bits of sand and shells glued together with mucus.

Down

2. The outer layer of a sponge.
4. A tiny creature that was discovered in the 1600s and has tiny hairs that flap back and forth.
6. The phylum in which sponges belong. Its name means "pore-bearer."
7. A partially transparent filter feeder that looks like a rubbery-looking cup with two openings. TWO WORDS
10. The phylum that contains earthworms and leeches, worms that are segmented with ring-like sections.
11. Fresh water flatworms.
12. One of the sea squirt's openings that sucks water into the animal. TWO WORDS
14. When something is made up of only one cell.
15. Animals that must consume food to live.
16. The spikes on a sponge that serve as its defense.
20. The marine flatworm uses this type of colorful defense so as to fool predators into thinking it is not a tasty meal, looking like an animal that is poisonous.

AQUATIC ANIMALS MINIBOOK

LESSON 13

Paste your Interesting Aquatic Animals Matchbook onto this page.

DIVE DEEPER

Lesson 13

Watch *Blue Planet: Seas of Life* Collection

Now that you have completed your course, I want to recommend my all time favorite DVD collection on sea creatures. It's called ***Blue Planet***. By watching this now, you will understand in great detail many of the things you will see. It will also serve as a fantastic review of your adventures through the creatures of the sea.

Watch Disneynature film *Oceans*

This film by Disney boldly chronicles the mysteries that lie beneath the oceans. Featuring spectacular never before seen imagery captured by the latest underwater technologies, ***Oceans*** offers an unprecedented look beneath the sea.

Book and DVD Suggestions

God Created the Sea Life of the World by Earl & Bonita Snellenberger. A Christian book on the various aspects of sea life.

Aquarium Guide: A Bible-based handbook to the aquarium by Answers in Genesis. Sharks, eels, shrimp, and so much more! This Creator-honoring guide features more than 100 creatures. Learn incredible facts and design features of fascinating water-dwelling animals all across our world.

The Ocean Book by Frank Sherwin. You'll be amazed by what lies beneath the surface of the world's oceans! Learn of the mysteries that lurk in the darkness thousands of feet below and join the adventure as the depths of the oceans are explored in this fascinating full-color book.

Marvels of Creation: Sensational Sea Creatures by Buddy and Kay Davis. This spectacular book by AiG staffers brings the world of the sea alive in a unique and colorful way. Features beautiful photographs of 30 animals from around the world, along with a page of facts and commentary about each creature.

Voice of the Deep: Moody Science Classics Series (DVD). The "silent deep" is not so silent after all. Take a trip beneath the sea to discover many strange facts about a little-known world.

*Be aware that some titles may contain evolutionary content

MY AQUATIC ANIMAL PROJECT

LESSON 13

What I did:

What I learned:

Scientific Speculation Sheet

Desalination

Lesson 13

Name__________________________ Date _____________

Materials Used:

Procedure:

Hypothesis:

Results:

Conclusion:

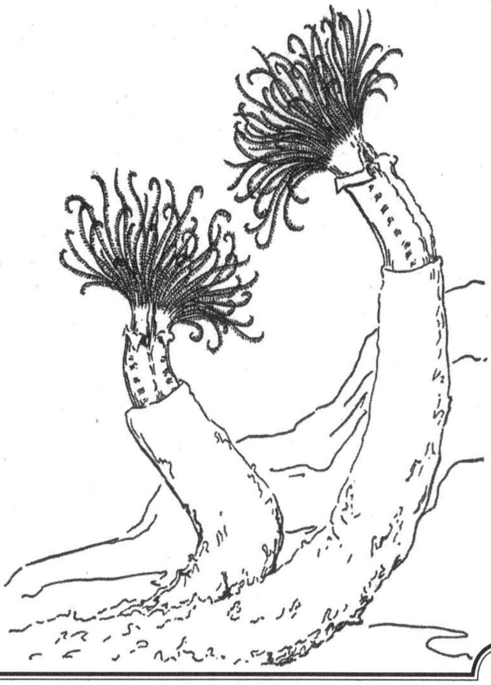

Name ______________________________ Date__________

Final Review Questions

1. What do we call the circular patterns that surface currents form in the ocean?
2. What is the principle cause of the ocean's tides?
3. Name the two kinds of whales.
4. What is the name of the hole on top of the whale's head through which the whale breathes?
5. What do we call newborn and young whales?
6. What is another name for a killer whale?
7. Name the pinnipeds about which you have learned.
8. Name a difference between true seals and sea lions.
9. Which pinniped has two teeth that grow extremely long?
10. Where can manatees be found?
11. Which animals are considered herps?
12. How are reptiles different from mammals?
13. Why are sea turtles considered an endangered species?
14. Name a difference between reptiles and amphibians.
15. What are gastroliths?
16. Why might there be so many sea creature fossils all over the earth (even on high mountain tops)?
17. Name the three kinds of fish.
18. Which fins are located on the top of a fish?
19. Which fins are located on the side of a fish?
20. Which fin is the tail fin on a fish?
21. Name a kind of fish that is cartilaginous.
22. What does the ampullae of Lorenzini sense?
23. What do we call animals that have jointed feet and legs, such as crabs and lobsters?
24. What is the tiny shrimp-like keystone species that many other sea creatures depend upon called?
25. What is it called when a crustacean sheds its exoskeleton to grow larger?

26. Which crustacean attaches itself to other sea creatures or objects in the water with a hard glue that is difficult to get off?
27. Which bivalves produce pearls?
28. Which mollusk is a filter feeder?
29. What do gastropods eat?
30. What is conchology?
31. Which gastropod does not have an external shell, and is usually characterized by flamboyant colors?
32. What does the word "cephalopod" mean?
33. What four cephalopods were discussed in the book?
34. How do cephalopods move through the water?
35. How many arms does a squid have?
36. What is the word for more than one octopus?
37. What are some defense mechanisms of cephalopods?
38. What is the correct name for a starfish?
39. What does it mean to regenerate?
40. How do sea cucumbers protect themselves?
41. Name the cnidarians that have dangling tentacles.
42. Which cnidarians are in the class called anthozoa, which means flower animal?
43. Which fish finds protection inside the sea anemone?
44. Name the two kinds of coral.
45. How do scientists determine whether a microscopic creature is a plant or animal?
46. What do we call animals that stick to one spot?
47. What is the sponge's skeleton made up of?
48. Name one kind of water worm.
49. What is another name for wheel animals?
50. What is another name for water bears?

VOCABULARY CROSSWORD SOLUTIONS

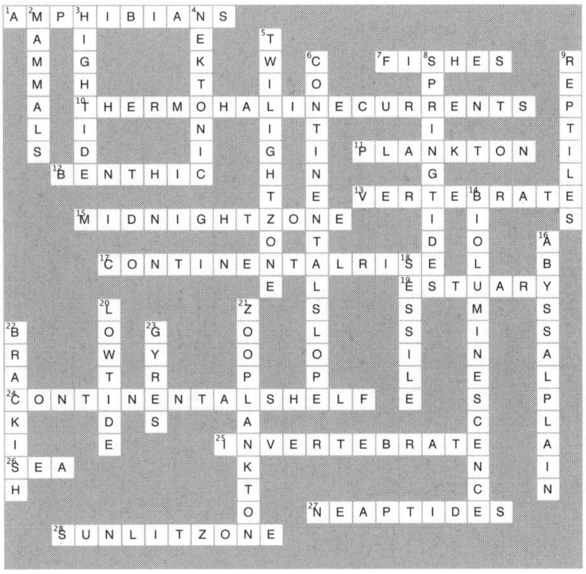

Lesson 1

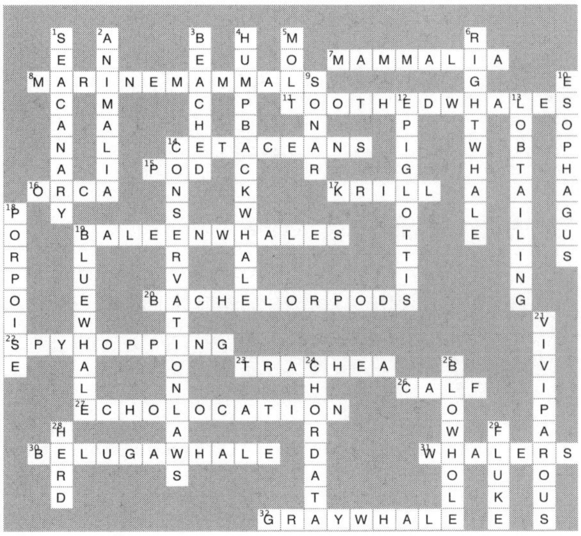

Lesson 2

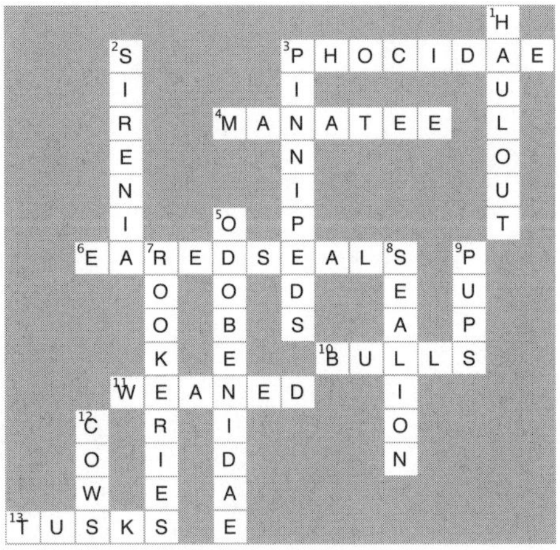

Lesson 3

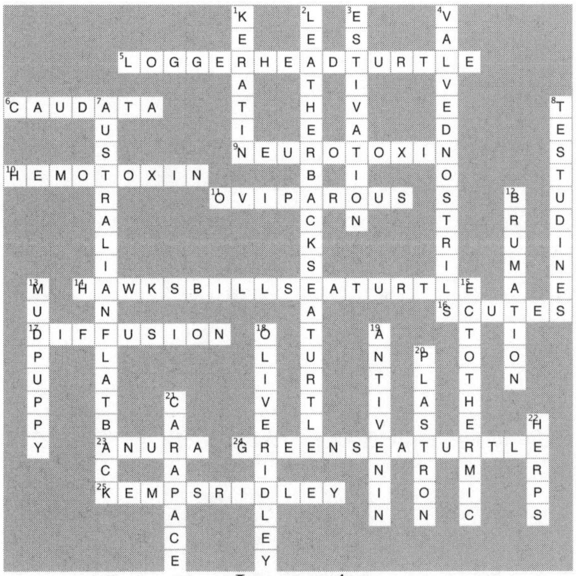

Lesson 4

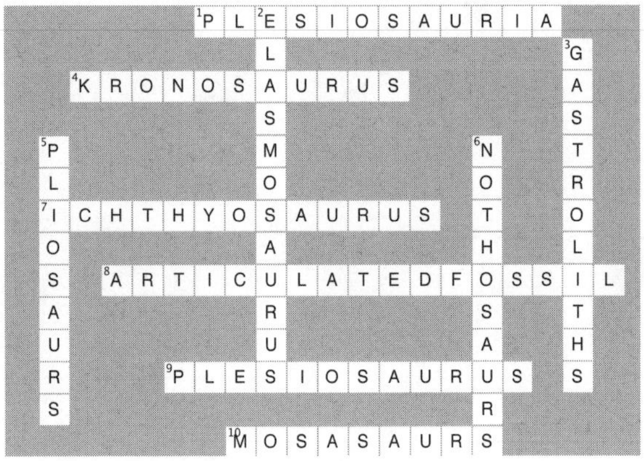

Lesson 5

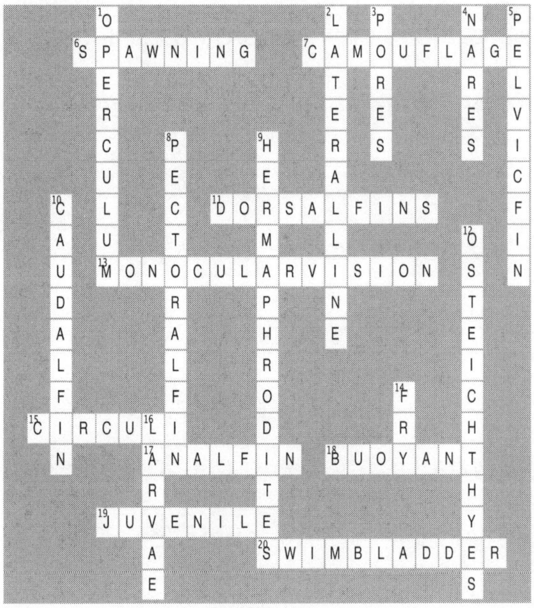

Lesson 6

VOCABULARY CROSSWORD SOLUTIONS

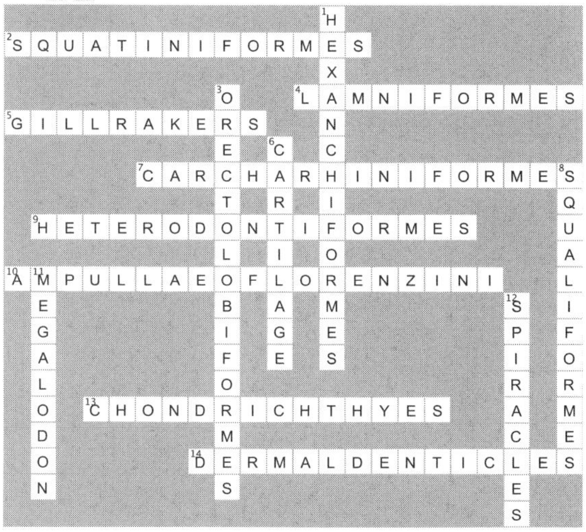

Lesson 7

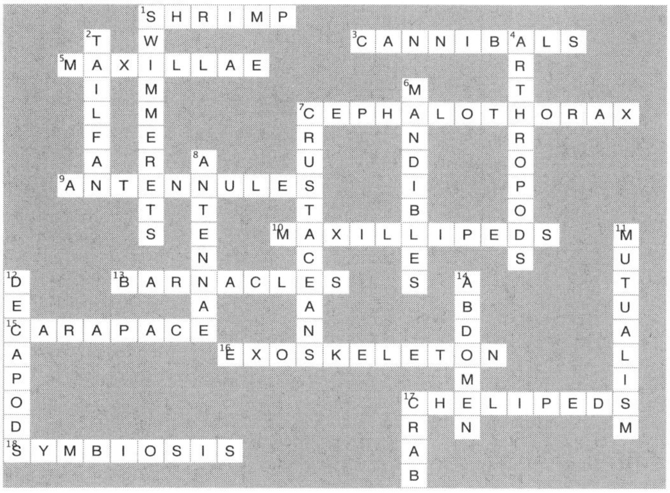

Lesson 8

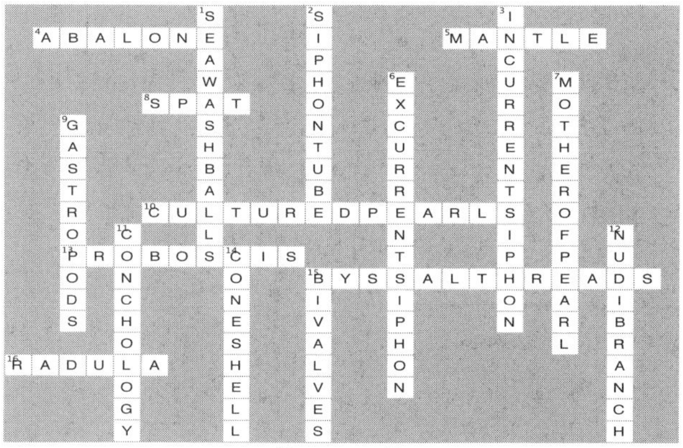

Lesson 9

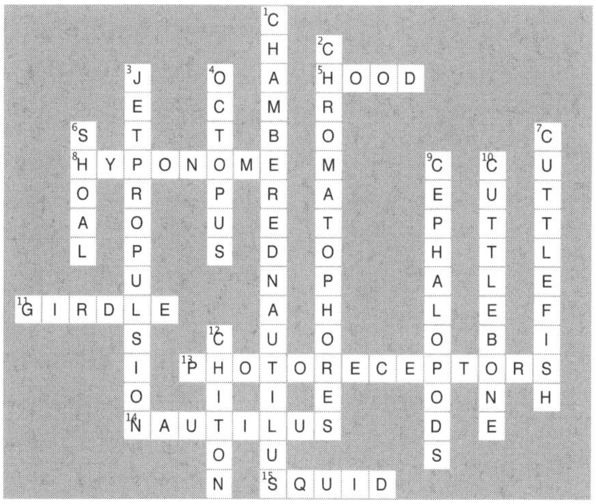

Lesson 10

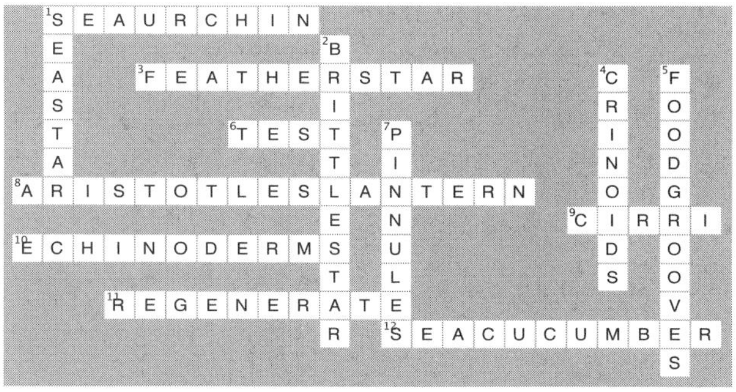

Lesson 11

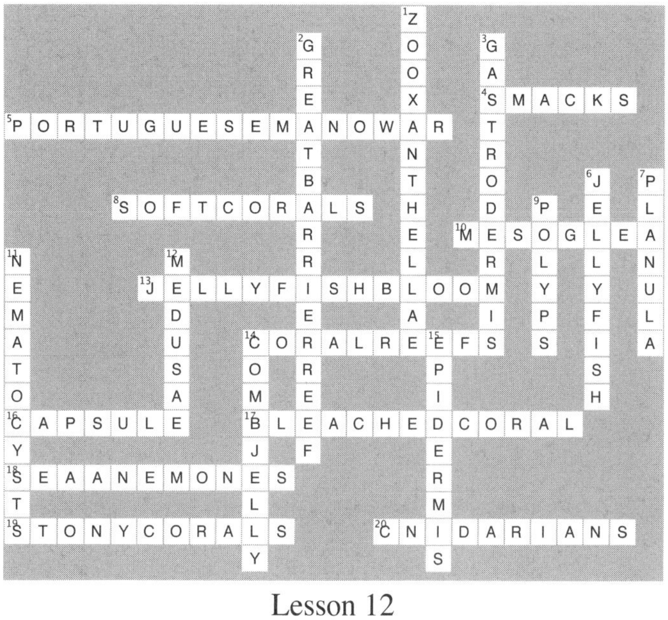

Lesson 12

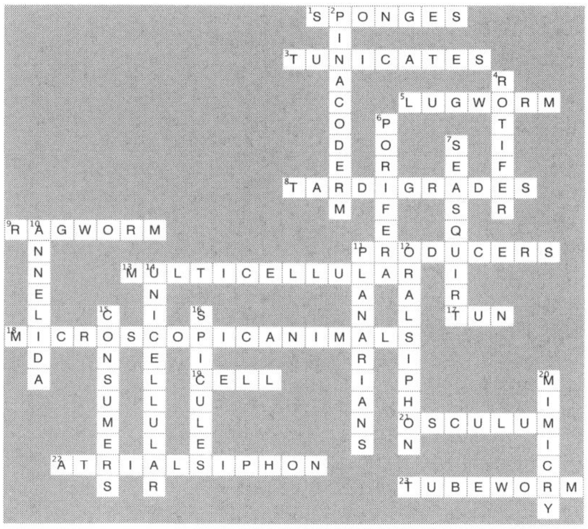

Lesson 13

Name ______________________________ Date ____________

Final Review Solutions

1. Gyres
2. The moon
3. Baleen whales and toothed whales
4. A blowhole
5. Calves
6. Orca
7. Seals, sea lions, walruses and sea cows
8. Answers my vary: Sea lions have small ear flaps, while seals do not have external ear flaps. Sea lions have the ability to "walk" on their flippers, while seals cannot support themselves on their flippers.
9. A walrus
10. In warm, fresh water rivers and salty oceans, such as the rivers and ocean around Florida.
11. Reptiles and amphibians (Specific animals are acceptable answers.)
12. Answers may vary: Mammals are warm blooded or endothermic, give birth to live young, and nurse their young. They also have hair, not scales.
13. Answers may vary: They are considered endangered because their numbers are dwindling. This is because, the journey to their breeding grounds is long and full of danger. Many dangers are present for the incubating eggs. Many dangers are present for the hatched turtles, and few hatchlings make it.
14. Answers may vary: Reptiles have dry scaly skin, lay eggs on dry ground, and the young look similar to the adults. Amphibians can breathe and drink through their skin.
15. Stomach stones that early reptiles (and other animals) swallowed to help grind food in their stomachs for digestion
16. Noah's flood, the deluge
17. Bony fish, cartilaginous fish, jawless fish
18. The dorsal fins
19. The pectoral fins
20. The caudal fin
21. Answers may vary: shark, sting ray, lamprey or hagfish
22. Electric impulses in the water, electricity
23. Arthropods (Crustaceans is an acceptable answer.)
24. Krill
25. Molting or molt
26. The barnacle
27. Clams and oysters (and a few other bivalves)
28. The bivalve
29. Bivalves, dead, dying or decaying creatures, algae and food waste
30. The study of shells
31. The nudibranch
32. Head foot
33. The octopus, squid, nautilus and cuttlefish
34. By jet propulsion
35. 10
36. Octopuses
37. Camouflage, ink, poison, shell (nautilus)
38. A sea star
39. To regrow body parts that are lost due to injury
40. By vomiting their insides and escaping
41. Medusae (Jellyfish and man-o-war are also acceptable.)
42. Sea anemones
43. The clown fish
44. Stony and soft
45. An animal is a multicellular creature that consumes food. A plant is a multicellular object that produces its own food. It does not consume other objects.
46. Sessile
47. Tiny spikes called spicules
48. Answers my vary: lugworm, flatworm, planarian, tubeworm, bristle worm, leech
49. Rotifers
50. Tardigrades

MY ZOOLOGY FIELD TRIP

Place: Date:

The purpose of this field trip:

What I saw/did on this trip:

What I learned:

My favorite part:

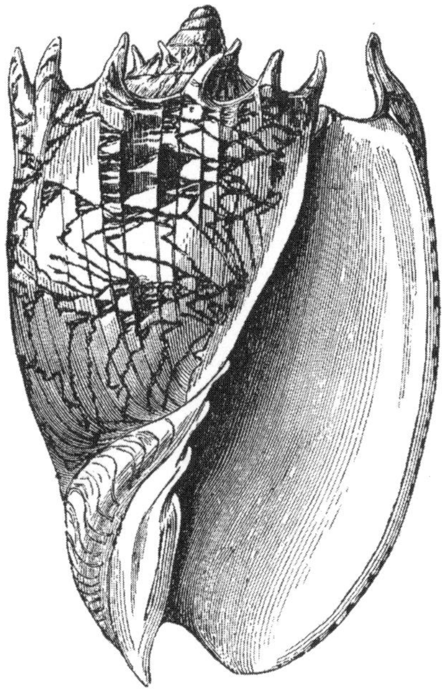

MY ZOOLOGY FIELD TRIP

Place: Date:

The purpose of this field trip:

What I saw/did on this trip:

What I learned:

My favorite part:

MY ZOOLOGY FIELD TRIP

Place: Date:

The purpose of this field trip:

What I saw/did on this trip:

What I learned:

My favorite part:

MY ZOOLOGY FIELD TRIP

Place: Date:

The purpose of this field trip:

What I saw/did on this trip:

What I learned:

My favorite part:

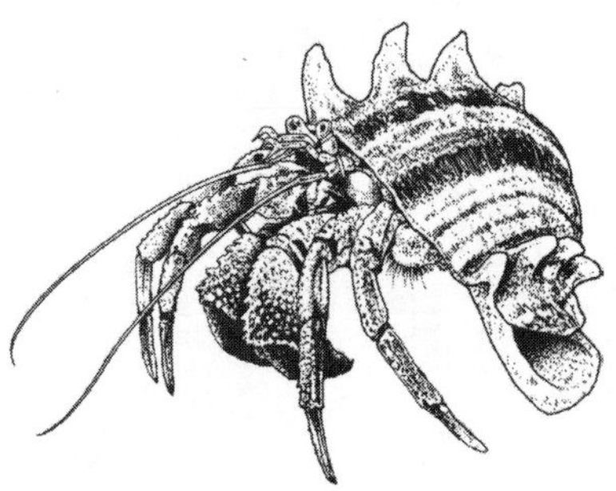

MY ZOOLOGY FIELD TRIP

Place: Date:

The purpose of this field trip:

What I saw/did on this trip:

What I learned:

My favorite part:

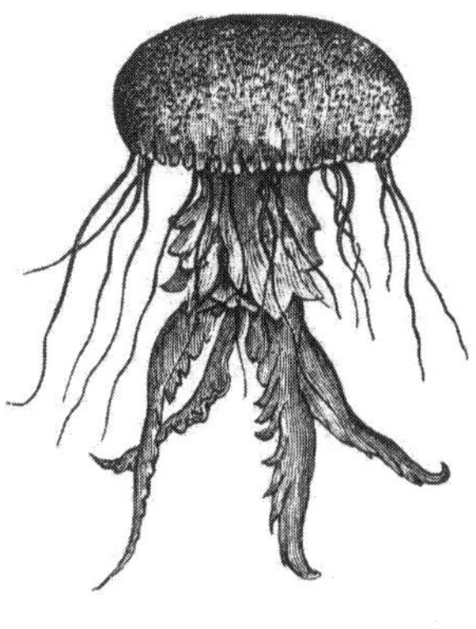

MY ZOOLOGY FIELD TRIP

Place: Date:

The purpose of this field trip:

What I saw/did on this trip:

What I learned:

My favorite part:

MY ZOOLOGY FIELD TRIP

Place: Date:

The purpose of this field trip:

What I saw/did on this trip:

What I learned:

My favorite part:

MY ZOOLOGY FIELD TRIP

Place: Date:

The purpose of this field trip:

What I saw/did on this trip:

What I learned:

My favorite part:

MY ZOOLOGY FIELD TRIP

Place: Date:

The purpose of this field trip:

What I saw/did on this trip:

What I learned:

My favorite part:

MY ZOOLOGY FIELD TRIP

Place: Date:

The purpose of this field trip:

What I saw/did on this trip:

What I learned:

My favorite part:

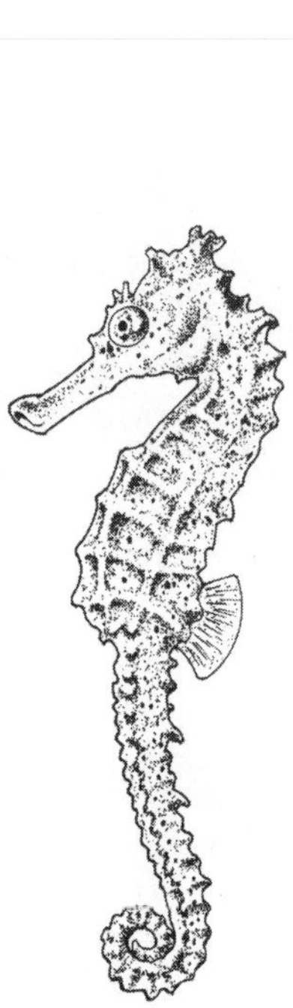

CREATION CONFIRMATION MINIATURE BOOK

(Instructions on back)

It's important to remember all you've learned about God and Creation in this course. This Creation Confirmation Book will enable you to recall and record all your learning.

Instructions:

1. Cut out the Creation Confirmation Book rectangles on pages A1 and A3 along the dotted lines. **Do not cut the gold fold lines!**
2. Fold the pages along the gold lines.
3. Place the pages inside the blue cover of the book.
4. Open the book to the middle and staple it along the center.
5. As you work through each lesson of the course, write down what you learn about God, the Bible and Creation.
6. Keep your Creation Confirmation Book inside your zoology book as a bookmark and a reminder to write down the things you learn.

EXTRA MINIATURE BOOKS

If you would like to record any additional information about swimming creatures not included in the other miniature books, here are a few extra miniature books for you to use.

Cut out the miniature books along the dotted lines. **Do not cut the black fold lines!** Record any additional information you've learned about zoology 2 not included in the other miniature books. Fold your books and glue the back covers of the books onto the paste page of the topic you have written about.

Glue this side of the book to your paste page.

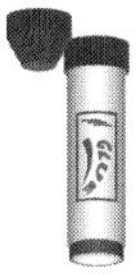

Glue this side of the book to your paste page.

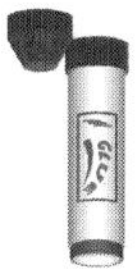

Glue this side of the book to your paste page.

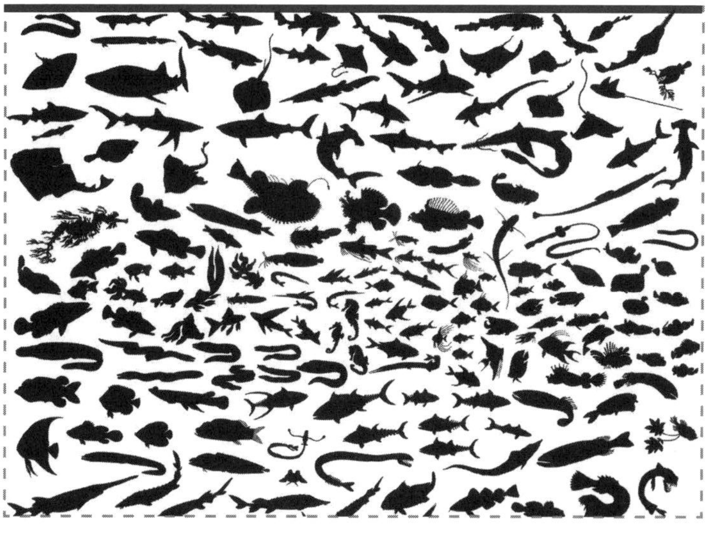

AQUATIC ANIMALS & THE OCEAN TAB BOOK

Instructions:

1. Cut out the tabbed rectangles on this and the next two pages. Fold the water cover page along the center fold line.
2. Fold the aqua mobility and tides page along the center line so the words "aqua mobility" are on the outside at the top. Place this page inside the water cover page.
3. Fold the currents and aquatic animals page along the center fold line so the words "aquatic animals" are on top and "currents" is below "aquatic animals." Place this page in the center of the book so the tabs line up down the side of the book when it is closed.
4. Open the book and staple it down the center by inserting a stapler across half the book.
5. Write or draw what you learned about aquatic animals and the ocean on the pages of your book. Be sure to label the diagrams.
6. Glue your Aquatic Animals & the Ocean Tab Book onto your "Aquatic Animals Minibook" paste page *(**NJ p. 26**)*.

4

Aquatic Animals

Currents

6

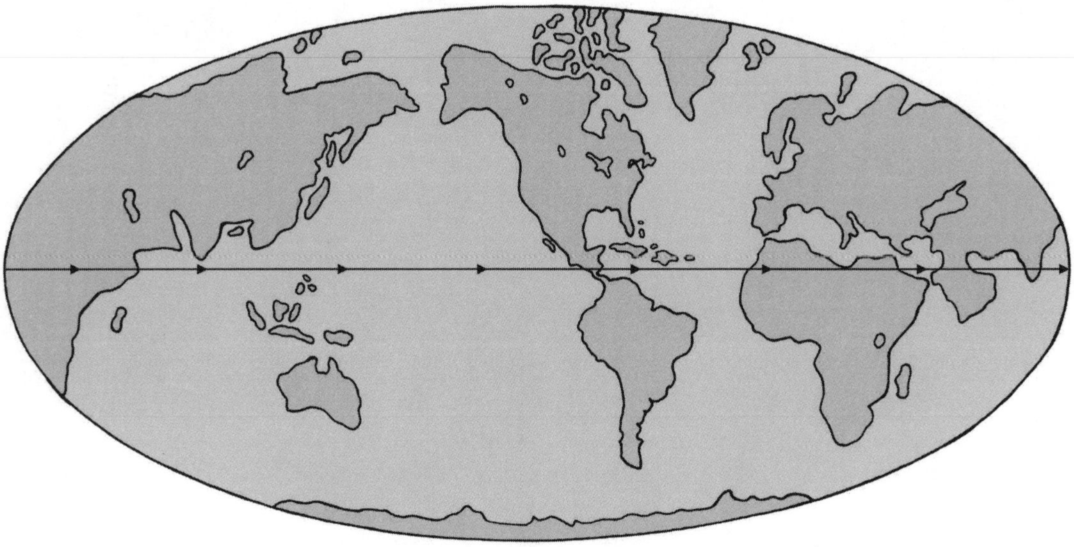

8

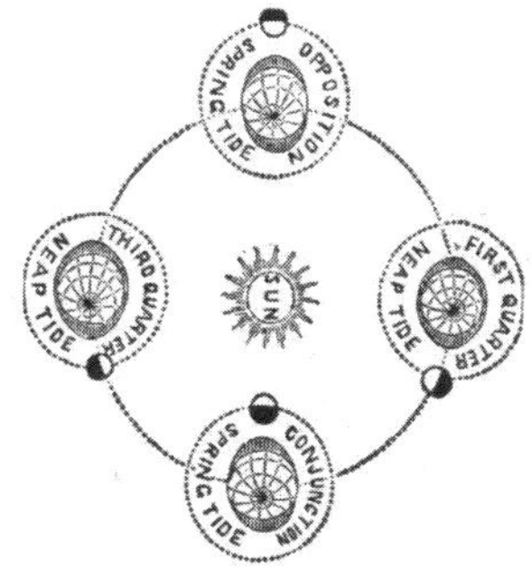
OPPOSITION
SPRING TIDE
FIRST QUARTER
NEAP TIDE
SUN
THIRD QUARTER
NEAP TIDE
CONJUNCTION
SPRING TIDE

Tides

Aqua
Mobility

2

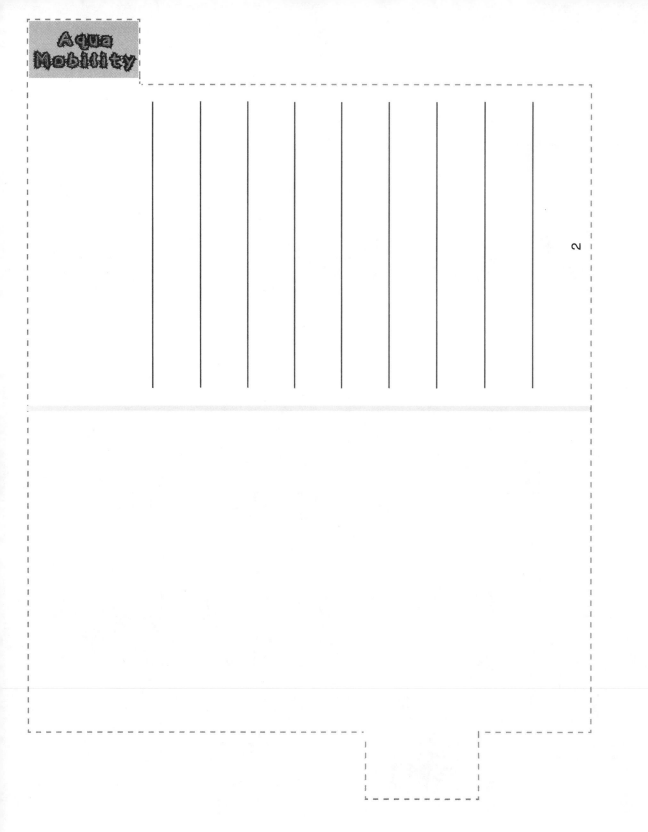

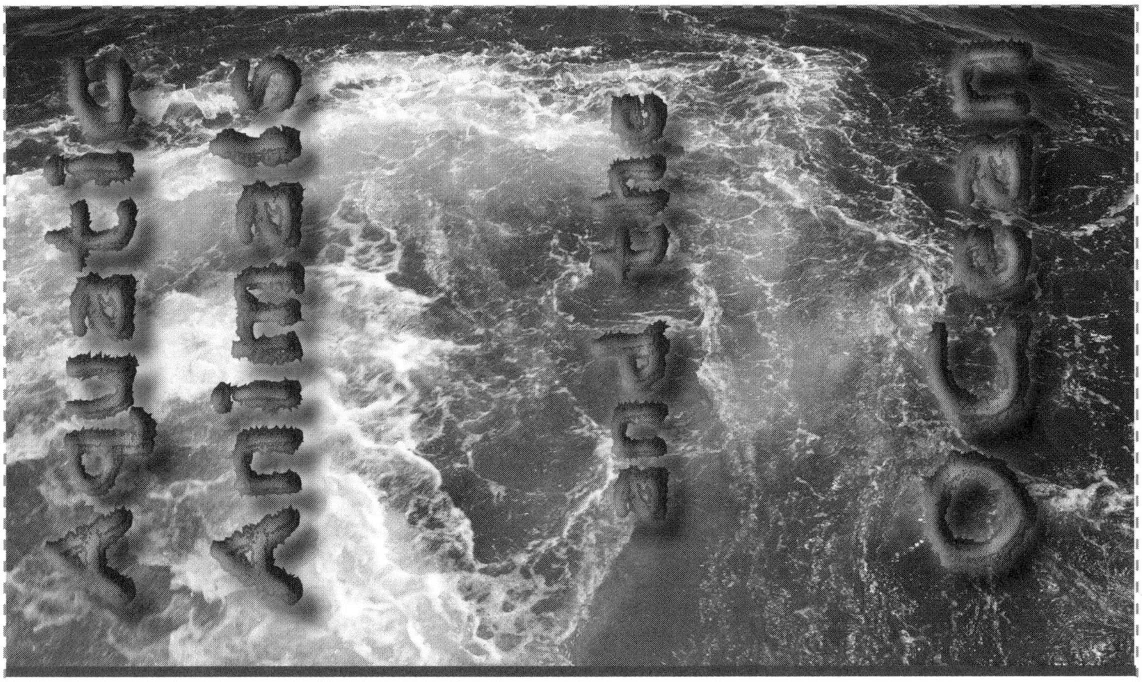
Aquatic
Animals
and the
Ocean

10

The Abyss

WHALES LAYERED BOOK

(Instructions on next page)

Stack smaller rectangle on top and line up here

Lobtailing

Stack smaller rectangle on top and line up here

Breaching

Stack smaller rectangle on top and line up here

Spyhopping

Stack smaller rectangle on top and line up here

Toothed Whales

Stack smaller rectangle on top and line up here

Baleen Whales

Stack smaller rectangle on top and line up here

Migration

Stack smaller rectangle on top and line up here

My Favorite Whale

Instructions:

1. Above each title, write the information requested about whales.
2. Cut out the eight rectangles along the outer edges.
3. Stack the rectangles with the largest on the bottom and the smallest on top.
4. Staple the rectangles along the top edge to create a layered book.
5. Lift the flaps to reveal things you've learned about whales.
6. Glue the bottom of your Whales Layered Book to your "Whales Minibook" paste page ***(NJ p. 41)***.

PINNIPEDS FLAP BOOKS

Instructions:

1. Cut out the Pinnipeds Flap Books along the outer edges.
2. Fold the triangular flaps inward along the yellow fold lines so they lay on top of the white squares.
3. Lift the flaps and write information you learned about each pinniped pictured on the flaps of each book.
4. Glue the books onto the "Pinnipeds Minibooks" paste page *(NJ p. 54)*.
5. Lift the flaps to remember what you learned about pinnipeds!

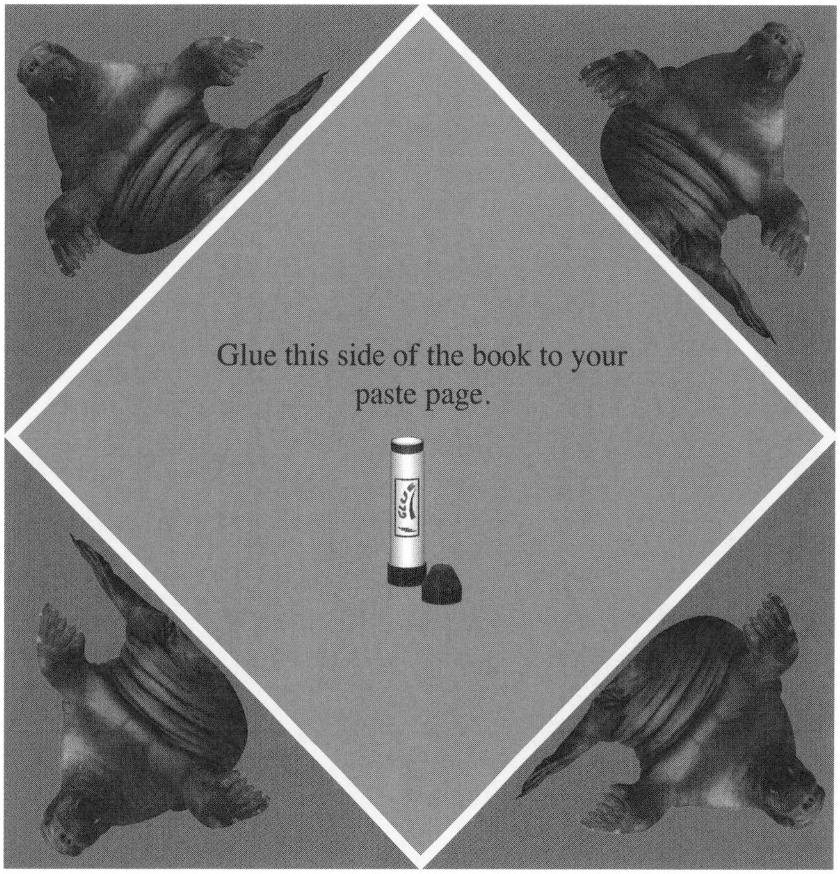
Glue this side of the book to your paste page.

Glue this side of the book to your paste page.

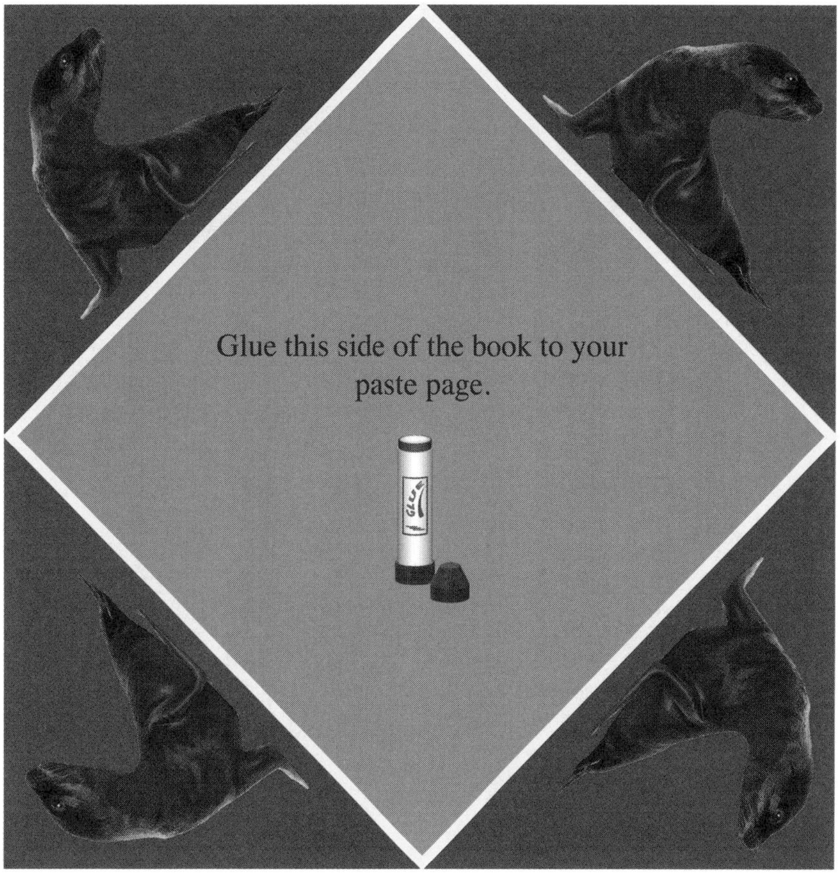
Glue this side of the book to your paste page.

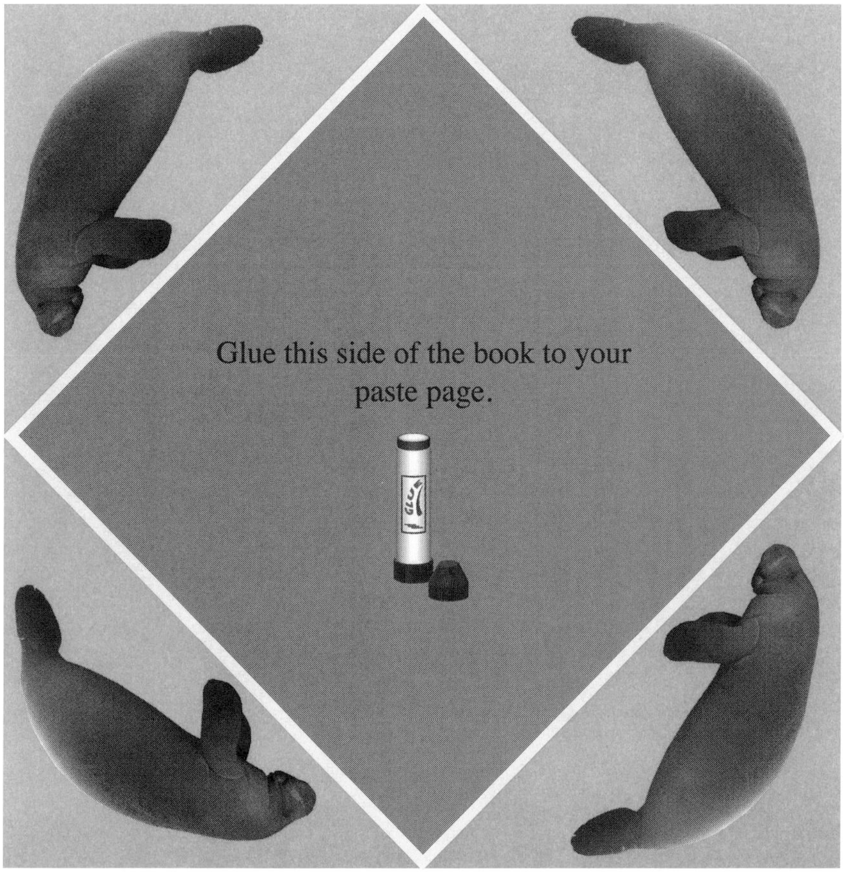
Glue this side of the book to your paste page.

HATCHING HERPS BOOKS

Instructions:

1. Cut out the eggs on this page (note: herp eggs are white or clear, but we used these speckled ones instead.) Cut along the yellow jagged lines.
2. Cut out the white circles on the next page along the dotted lines.
3. Glue the bottom halves of the eggs to the white circles along the bottom edges. Be sure to line glue along the bottom edges of the eggs only. This will make pockets in which you will insert your herps.
4. Cut out the herps along the outer edges and around the dotted lines, being sure to keep the animals connected. Fold the animals in half and write facts you learned about them on the insides. Place the herps inside the egg pockets.
5. Line up the top halves of the eggs with the bottom halves and punch brass fasteners through the yellow circles of the top halves of the eggs all the way through the bottom white circles. Fold the fasteners back to secure them.
6. Glue your Matching Herps Books to the "Herps Minibooks" paste page ***(NJ p. 68)***.
7. Open the cracked eggs to see and read about herps!

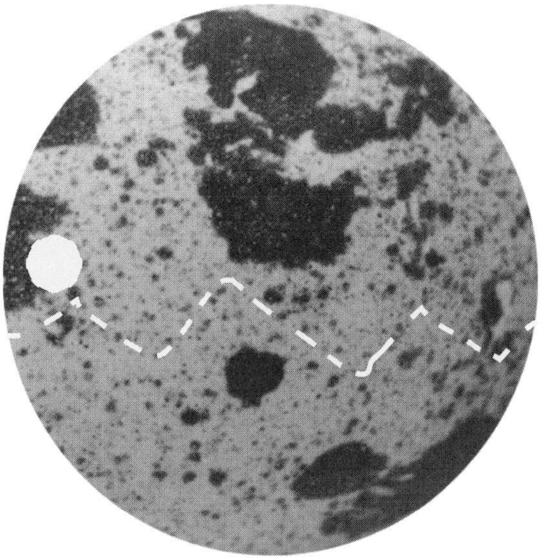
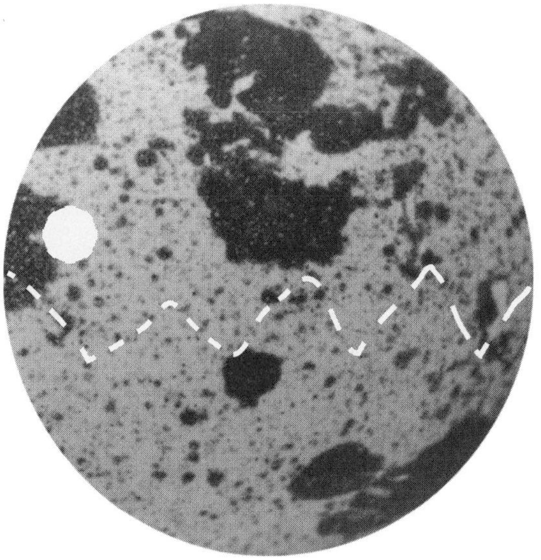
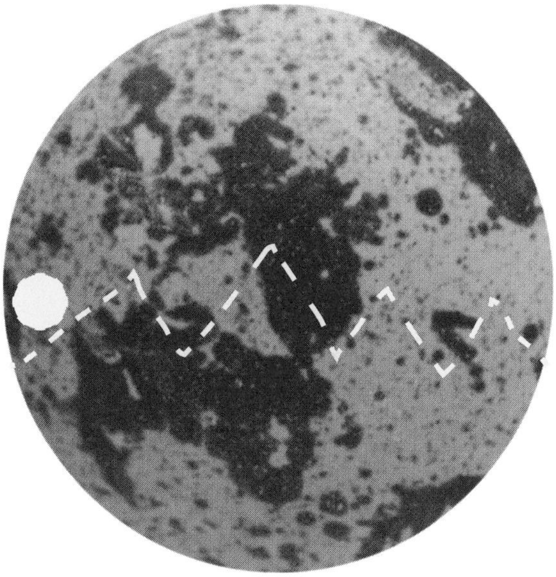
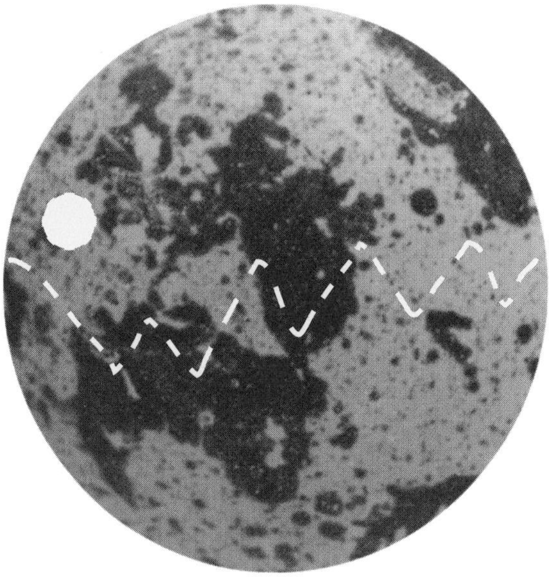
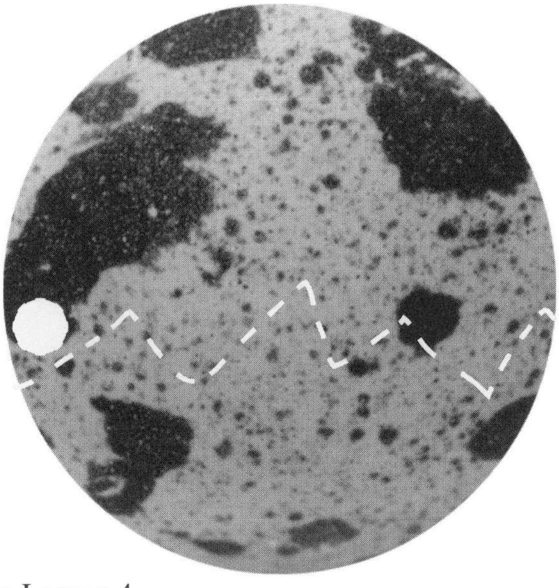
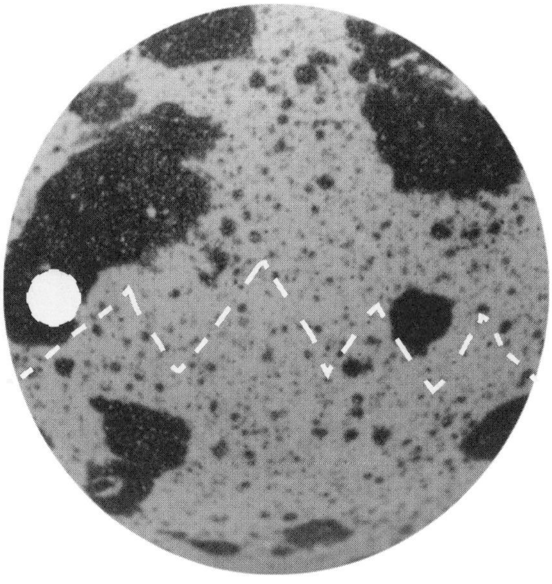

Place Glue along bottom edge only of each egg and glue to the circle

Place Glue along bottom edge only of each egg and glue to the circle

Place Glue along bottom edge only of each egg and glue to the circle

Place Glue along bottom edge only of each egg and glue to the circle

Place Glue along bottom edge only of each egg and glue to the circle

Place Glue along bottom edge only of each egg and glue to the circle

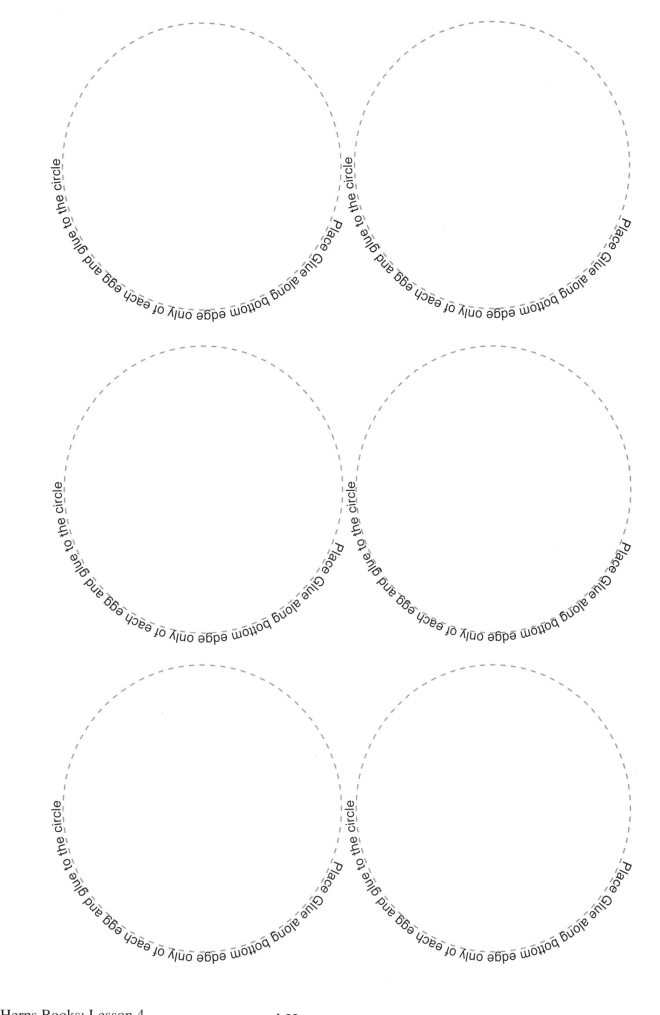

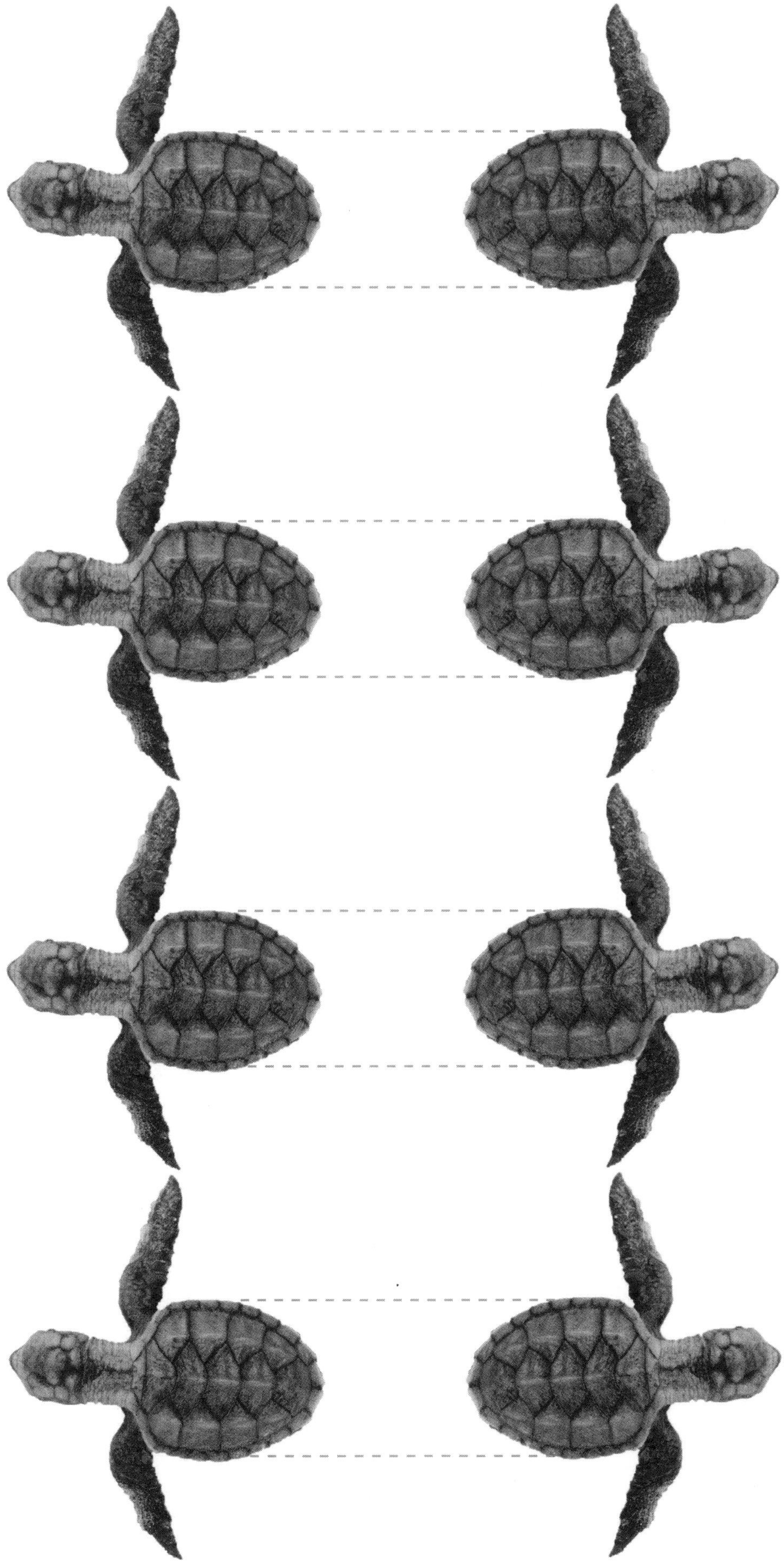

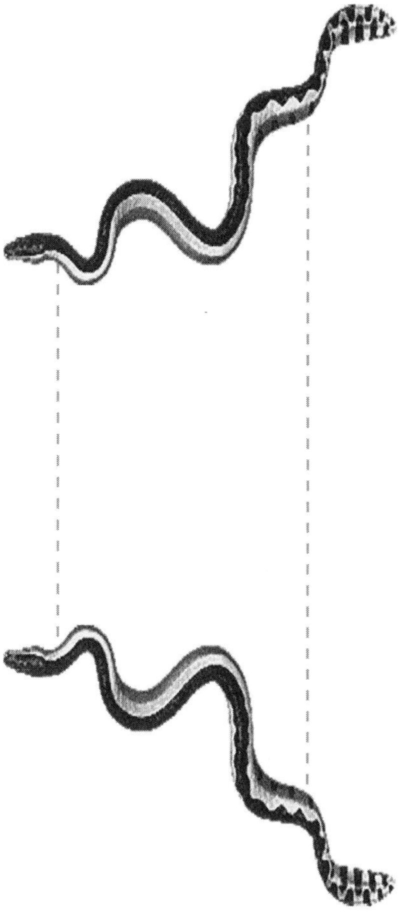

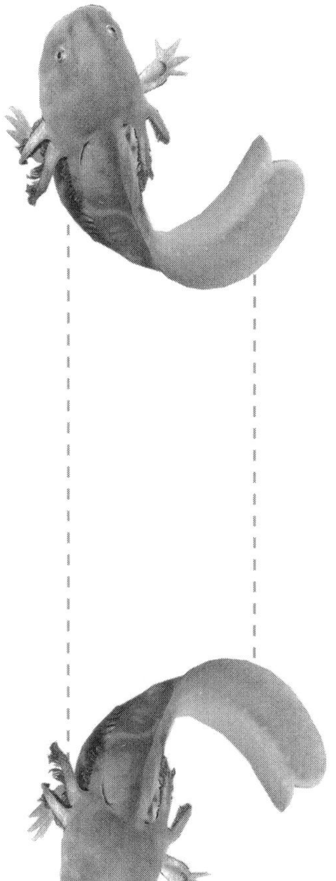

PRIMEVAL REPTILES WHEEL

Primeval Reptiles Circle

Instructions:

1. Cut out both the Fact Circle and the Primeval Reptiles Circle. Be sure to cut out the white empty space in the Primeval Reptiles Circle.
2. Place the Primeval Reptiles Circle on top of the Fact Circle, and insert a brass fastener in the center (on the gold spot) to secure the two circles.
3. Write something interesting you learned about each topic listed in the Fact Circle.
4. Dab glue on the bottom of the Fact Circle and glue your Primeval Reptiles Wheel onto the "Primeval Reptiles" paste page ***(NJ p. 98)***.
5. Turn the Primeval Reptiles Circle around to reveal the different facts about each topic.

Fact Circle

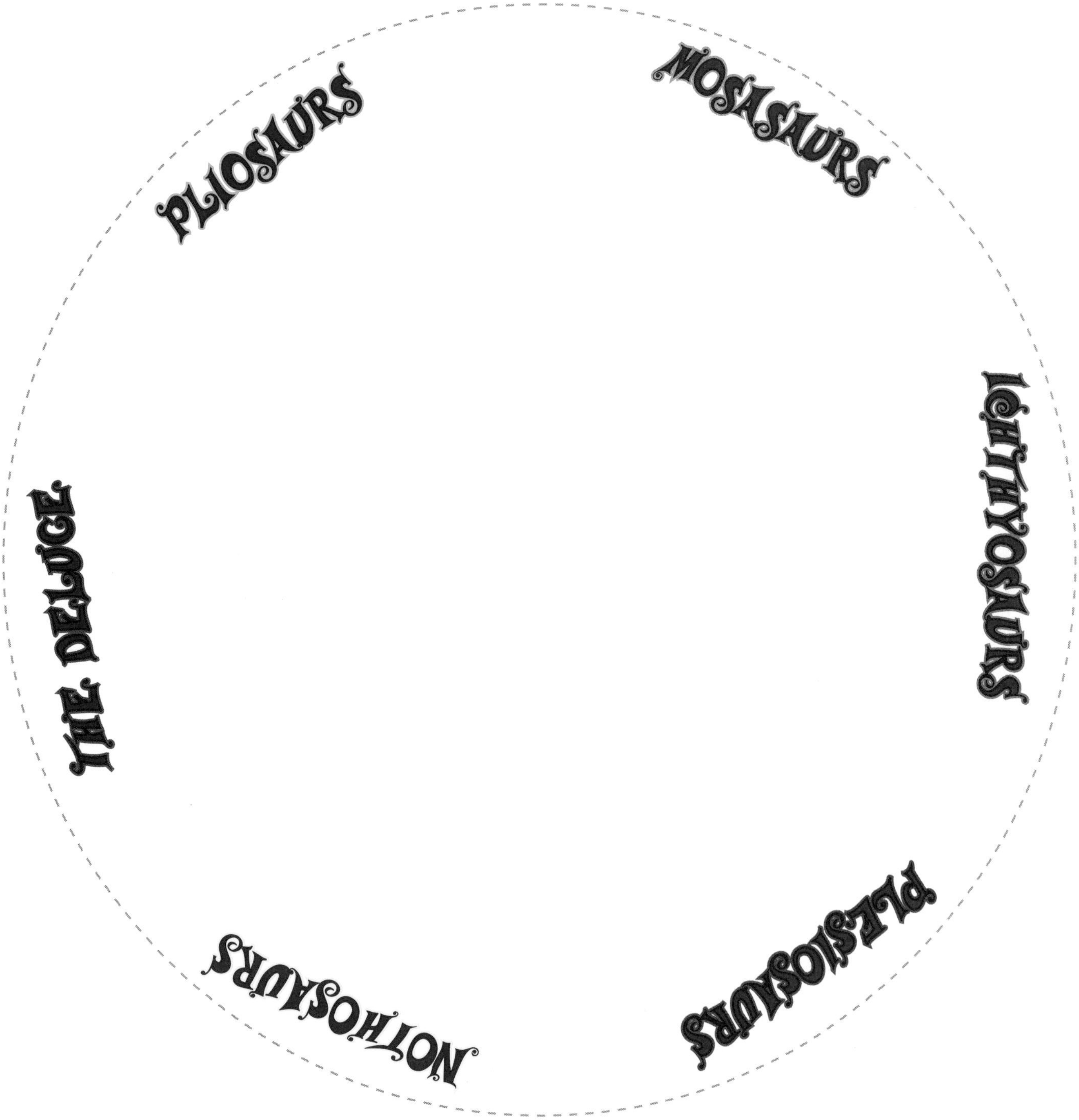

FISH BOWL PULL UP

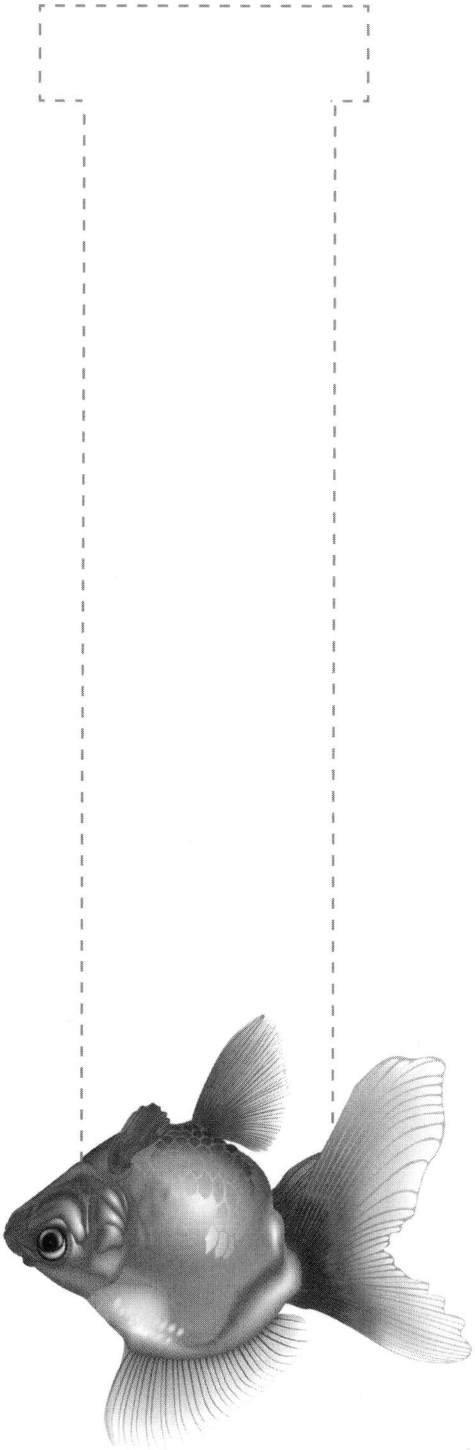

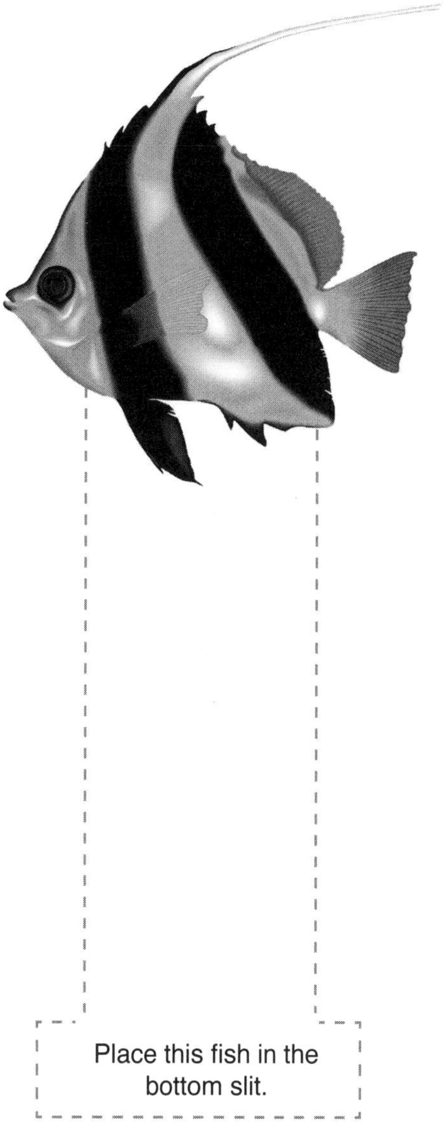
Place this fish in the bottom slit.

Instructions:

1. Cut out the fishes on this page and the next being sure to keep the strips attached to the fishes.
2. Write interesting facts you learned about fish on the strips.
3. Cut out the fish bowl scene along the yellow cut line on the left side of the page.
4. Cut slits along the five yellow cut lines in the fish bowl scene.
5. Slide the fishes into the slits so they appear to be floating in the water.
6. Glue the outer edges only of your Fish Bowl Pull Up onto the "Fishes Minibook" paste page *(**NJ p. 111**)*. Be sure not to glue down the page; only glue the outer edge so that you can slide the fishes up and down. Be certain not to glue the fishes' strips to the page.
7. Pull up the fishes to enjoy remembering all you learned!

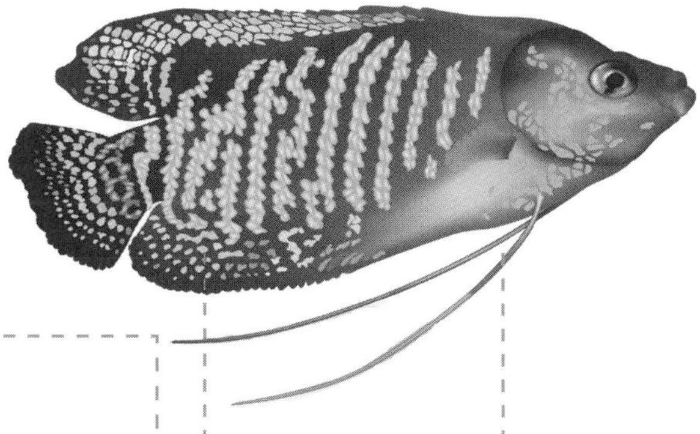

Place this fish in the top slit.

Place this fish in the bottom slit.

Fish Pull-up Facts

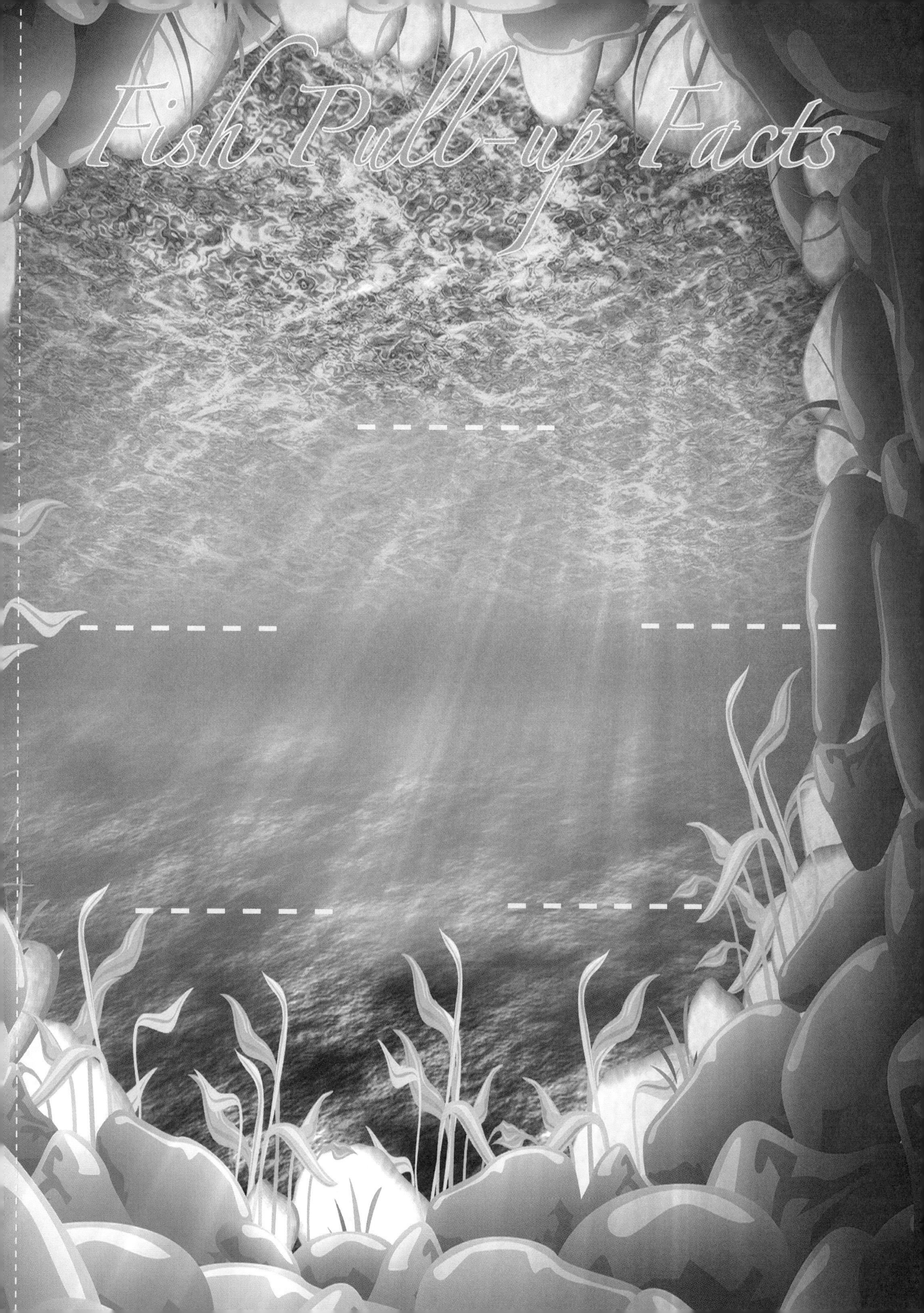

SHARKS AND RAYS POP UP BOOKS

Pull this tab forward. Crease. Glue lamprey here.

LAMPREY

Pull this tab forward. Crease. Glue hagfish here.

HAGFISH

Instructions:

1. Cut out the two rectangles on this page and the two on the next page. **Do not cut the grey fold lines!**
2. Write down what you learned about sharks, rays, lamprey and hagfish on the lines provided. Fold the rectangles inward along the center grey fold lines so that the titles are not visible.
3. Make four small cuts along the dashed lines in the center of each rectangle.
4. Open the paper up and gently pull each pop-up tab forward.
5. Crease the pop-up tabs with your fingers. Close the books to crease the pop-up tabs along the center line so that they are creased outward.
6. Cut out the four colored rectangle covers and cut around the outside of the pictures.
7. Fold the covers inward so that the titles are on the outside. Glue them to the outside of your lined rectangles to form the book covers.
8. Glue your pictures to the front of the pop-up tabs inside each book.
9. Glue your pop-up books to your "Sharks and Rays" paste page ***(NJ p. 123)***.
10. Open your books to see the pictures pop up, and enjoy reading all about sharks,rays, lamprey and hagfish.

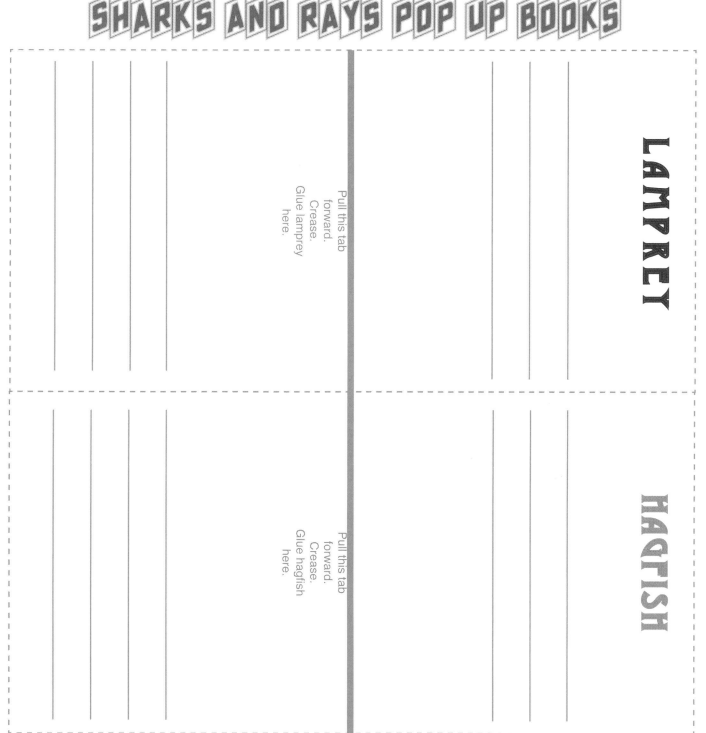

SHARK

Pull this tab
forward.
Crease.
Glue shark
here.

RAY

Pull this tab
forward.
Crease.
Glue ray here.

These are the covers for your pop-up books. Fold them inward along the center lines and glue them to the outside of your pop-up pages.

SHARK

RAY

These are the covers for your pop-up books. Fold them inward along the center lines and glue them to the outside of your pop-up pages.

HAGFISH

LAMPREY

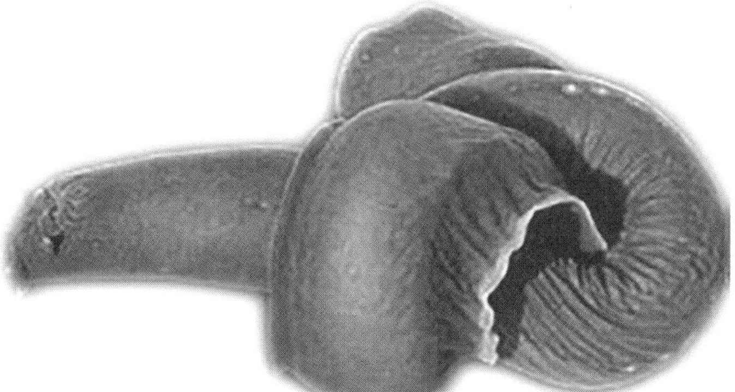

Hagfish

Lamprey

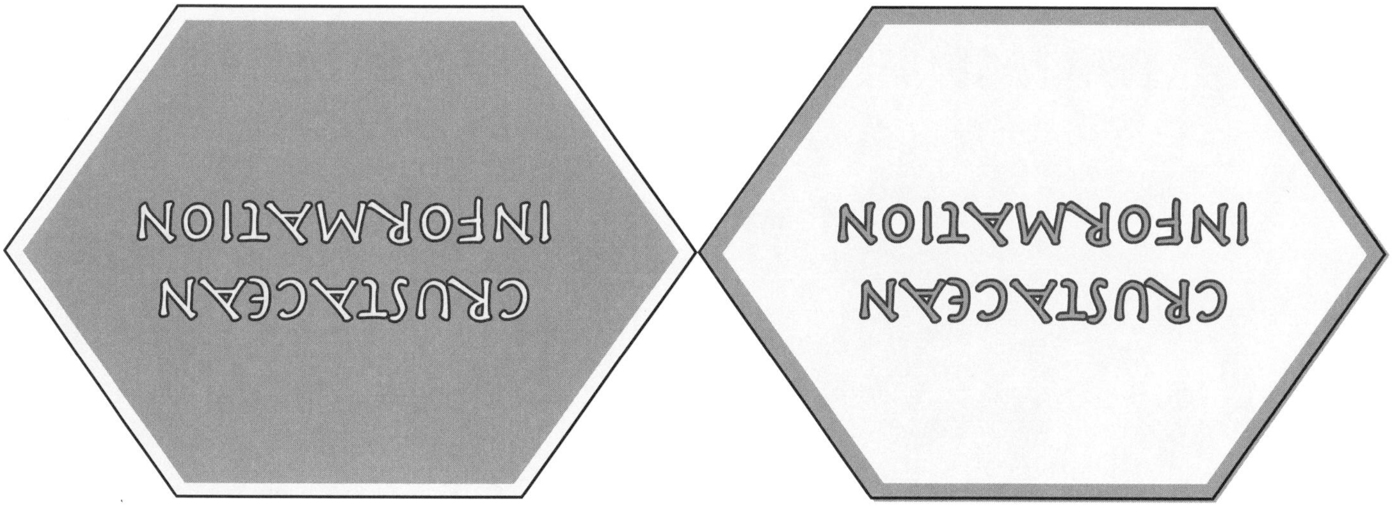

CRUSTACEAN ACCORDIION BOOK

Instructions:

1. Cut out the accordion books along the dotted lines. **Do not cut the yellow fold lines!**
2. Write information about the topics listed inside the books.
3. Fold the green and yellow crustacean title pages over so they appear as the top pages of the books.
4. Fold the remaining three shapes of the books back and forth like an accordion so that they are all folded up under the title pages.
5. Glue the bottoms of the books to your "Crustaceans Mini-books" paste page ***(NJ p. 135)***.

SHRIMP

LOBSTERS

KRILL

CRAYFISH

BARNACLES

CRABS

HORSESHOE CRABS

TRILOBITES

MOLLUSKS MINIATURE BOOKS

Instructions:

1. Cut out the Mollusks Miniature Books along the outside edges. **Do not cut the green fold lines!**
2. Fold your books along the green fold lines and write information you learned about mollusks, bivalves and gastropods inside the books.
3. Glue the bottoms of your Mollusks Miniature Books onto your "Mollusks Mini-books" paste page ***(NJ p. 148)***.

MOLLUSKS
GASTROPODS

CEPHALOPODS FAN

Instructions:

1. Cut out the Cephalopod Fan Pocket below being sure to cut along the dotted lines of the outer flaps. Fold the outer flaps inward.
2. Cut out each individual fan sheet on the next page.
3. Fill in the information requested under each topic.
4. Punch a hole in the bottom of each fan sheet on the white dot.
5. Stack your fan sheets on top of one another.
6. Secure the fan sheets at the bottom by inserting a brass fastener into the punch holes.
7. Put glue on the bottom and side flaps your Cephalopod Fan Pocket and paste the pocket onto your "Cephalopods Minibook" paste page ***(NJ p. 161)***.
8. Place your Cephalopods Fan in the pocket and remove it when you want to read all about cephalopods.

Fold inward and place glue along this flap to make a pocket

Fold inward and place glue along this flap to make a pocket

Fold inward and place glue along this flap to make a pocket

Octopus

Squid

Cuttlefish

Nautilus

ECHINODERMS POCKET

Fold inward and place glue along this flap to make a pocket.

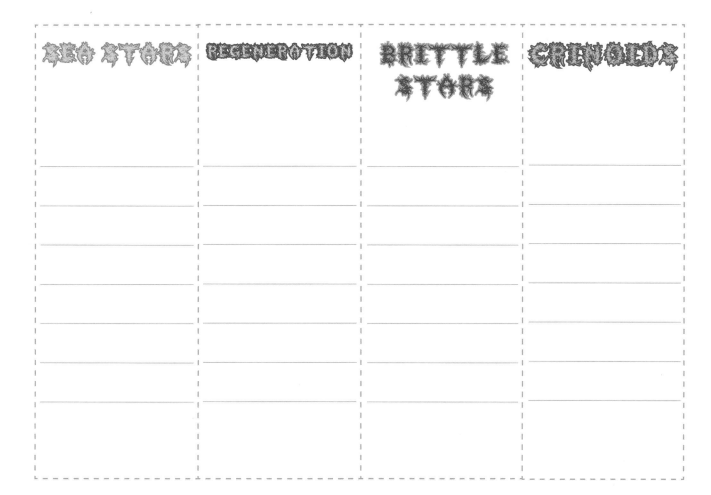

Fold inward and place glue along this flap to make a pocket.

Fold inward and place glue along this flap to make a pocket.

Instructions:

1. Cut out the Echinoderm Pocket to the left being sure to cut along the dotted lines of the outer flaps. Fold the flaps inward.
2. Cut out the fact cards on this page and the next.
3. Fill in information under the titles listed on each card.
4. Put glue on the bottom and side flaps of your Echinoderm Pocket and paste the pocket onto your "Echinoderms Minibook" paste page ***(NJ p. 175)***.
5. Insert the cards in your pocket. Pull them out whenever you want to read about echinoderms!

SEA STARS	REGENERATION	BRITTLE STARS	CRINOIDS

SEA URCHINS	SAND DOLLAR	SEA CUCUMBER	ECHINODERMS

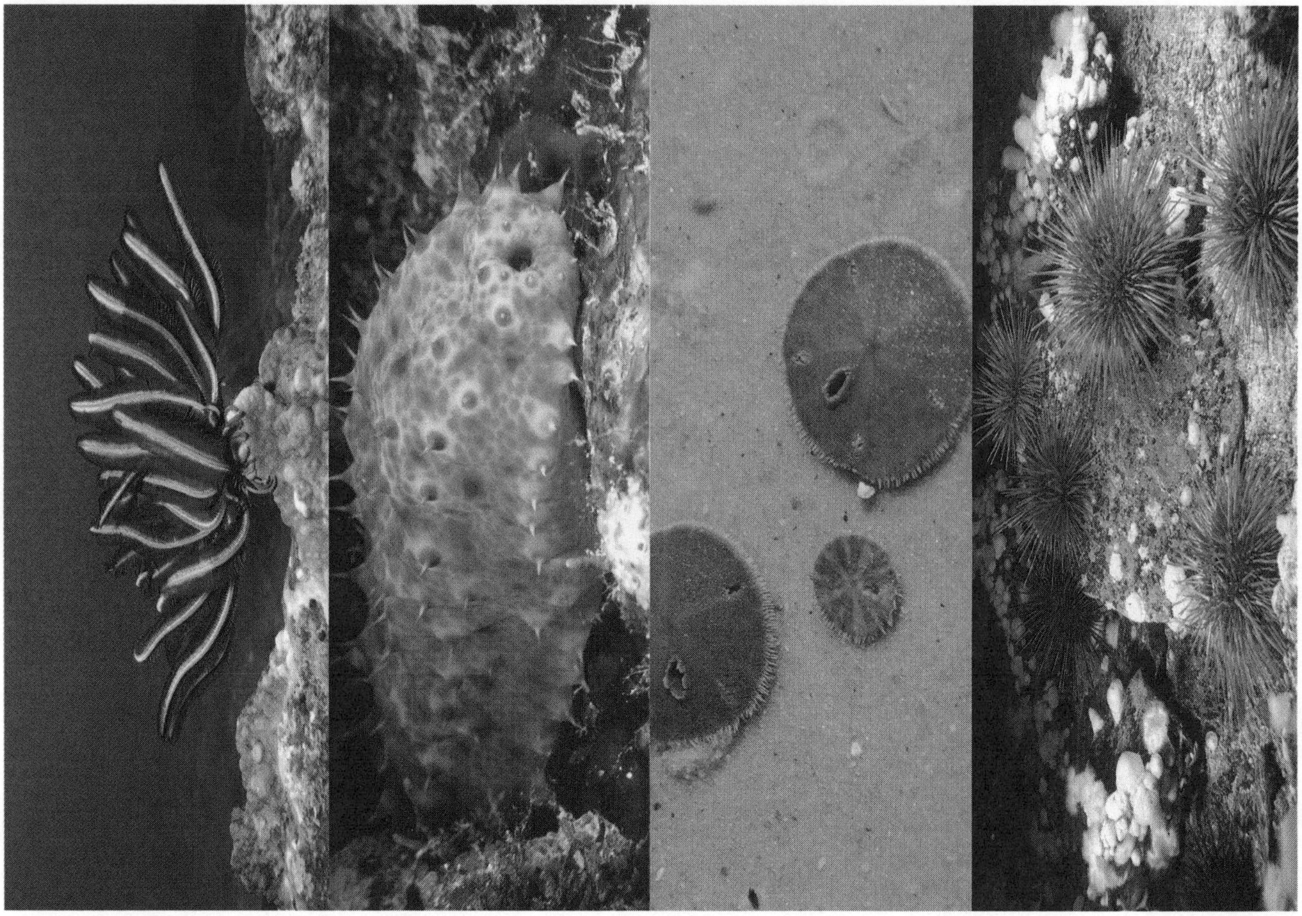

CNIDARIANS FLAP BOOK

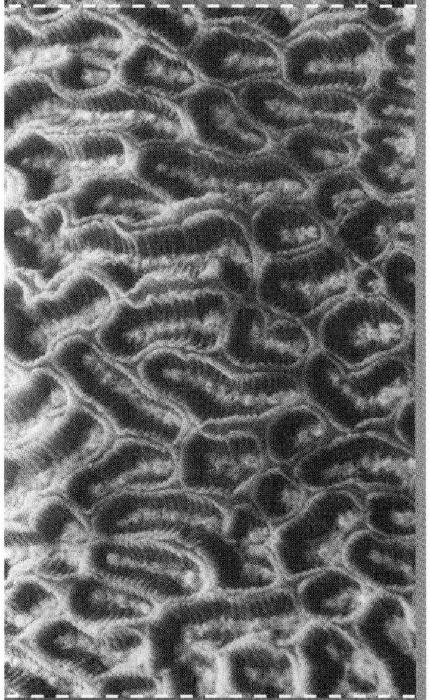

Instructions:

1. Cut out the large rectangle on this page along the dotted lines.
2. Cut between the images along the four dotted lines that divide the images. **Do not cut into the orange fold lines!**
3. Fold the colored rectangles away from you along the orange fold lines.
4. Turn over your Cnidarian Flap Book and lift the flaps.
5. Write information you learned about the cnidarians pictured on the flaps.
6. Glue this side (with these words) to your "Cnidarians Minibook" paste page ***(NJ p. 190)***.

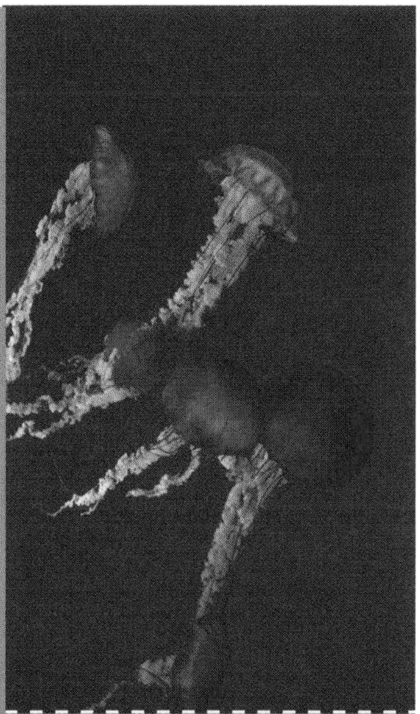

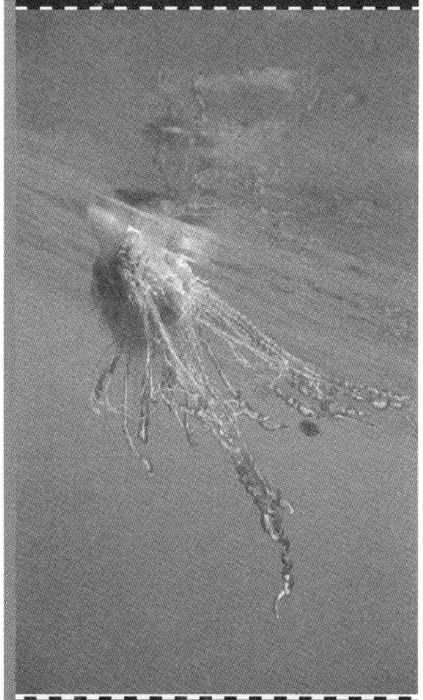

Cnidarian Facts

INTERESTING AQUATIC ANIMALS MATCHBOOK

This is the matchbook cover that will hold all your rectangular pages.

Instructions:

1. Cut out the matchbook cover along the dotted lines. **Do not cut the blue fold lines!**
2. Fold along the blue lines so that the large flap and the small flap face outward in the same direction.
3. Cut out the rectangles on this page and the next and fill in the information you learned about each topic.
4. Lift the large flap and place all the pages you created under the small flap.
5. With the large cover flap open and your pages under the small flap, staple your matchbook on the white line that crosses the center of the small flap. This will hold all your pages inside. **Do not staple the cover closed!**
6. Fold the large flap down and tuck it into the small flap, like a matchbook.
7. Glue this side (with these words) onto the "Aquatic Animals Minibook" paste page *(**NJ p. 203**)*.

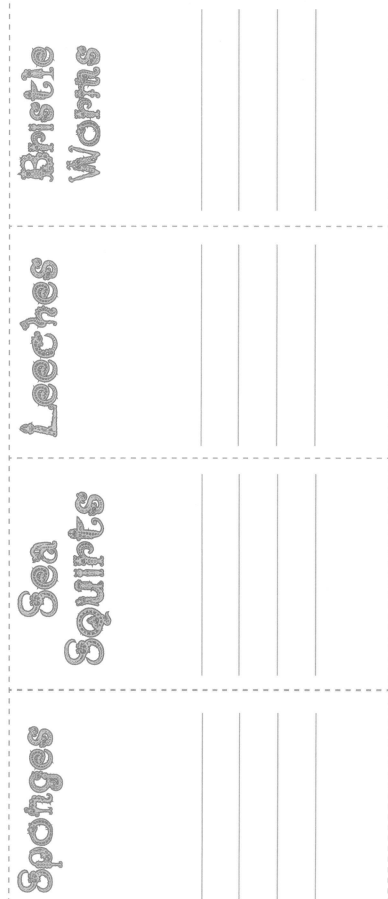

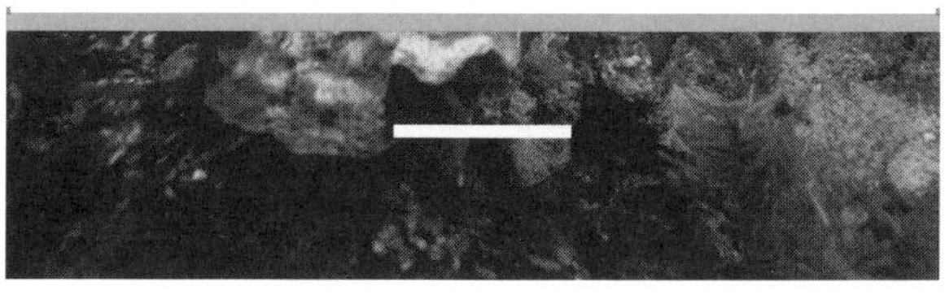

Bristle Worms

Leeches

Sea Squirts

Sponges

Flatworms

Rotifers

Tubeworms

Lugworms

Ragworms

Tardigrades